'**And so, ladies and gentlemen, we come to our final lot of the evening—and this one's going to be the most popular of all, I'm quite sure. Our very own Ginny!**'

Ginny rose to her feet, essaying a graceful curtsey in response to the applause. The bidding was lively, aided by Ginny, who laughingly encouraged it upwards with her hands. It quickly topped all the other prices and was still rising.

'Six hundred pounds, I'm bid!' Cornell enthused. 'Do I have any advance on that?' He lifted his gavel to crack it down. 'For the first time…'

Suddenly a laconic voice spoke from her own table. 'One thousand pounds.'

A ripple of surprise ran round the room—partly because of the amount of money being bid, but also because of who was doing the bidding. Oliver. Ginny felt a treacherous blush of pink colour her cheeks as she stared into those level dark eyes. Why was he doing this?

Every eye in the room turned back to Oliver as Cornell lifted his gavel. 'Any advance on one thousand pounds?' he queried doubtfully. 'For the first time… For the second time…' The clack of his gavel seemed to strike a sharp pain into Ginny's heart. 'Sold to Oliver Marsden.'

Susanne McCarthy grew up in South London but she always wanted to live in the country, and shortly after her marriage she moved to Shropshire with her husband. They live in a house on a hill with lots of dogs and cats. She loves to travel—but she loves to come home. As well as her writing, she still enjoys her career as a teacher in adult education, though she only works part-time now.

Recent titles by the same author:

HIS PERFECT WIFE

BRIDE
FOR SALE

BY
SUSANNE McCARTHY

MILLS & BOON®

All the characters in this book have no existence outside the imagination of the author, and have no relation whatsoever to anyone bearing the same name or names. They are not even distantly inspired by any individual known or unknown to the author, and all the incidents are pure invention.

First published in Great Britain 1998
Harlequin Mills & Boon Limited,
Eton House, 18-24 Paradise Road, Richmond, Surrey TW9 1SR

© Susanne McCarthy 1998

ISBN 0 263 81144 1

Set in Times Roman 10½ on 11½ pt.
01-9809-53662 C1

Printed and bound in Norway
by AiT Trondheim AS, Trondheim

CHAPTER ONE

'COUNT DRACULA, Oliver?' Ginny Hamilton's fine green eyes sparkled with mischief. 'It's supposed to be a fancy dress ball, you know, not "Come As Your True Self".'

Oliver Marsden conceded a dry smile. With his raven-black hair swept back from his high, autocratic forehead, and a silk-lined opera cape swirling from his wide shoulders, he did indeed bear a striking resemblance to the vampire Count. And he exuded the same kind of lethal charisma.

'I could say the same of you,' he countered. 'Don't tell me—Scarlett O'Hara, taking Atlanta by storm? And just as set on raising a scandal, no doubt.'

'Why, I do declare!' Ginny laughed, affecting a languid Southern drawl as she swept him a mocking curtsey, the soft green velvet of her wide crinoline skirt billowing around her. 'After all, I do have a reputation to uphold!'

'I doubt you'll have much difficulty doing that.' From his commanding height, his dark eyes lingered with sardonic appreciation over the creamy ripeness of her breasts, displayed to stunning effect by the sweepingly low neckline of her dress. 'Particularly in that creation. It's quite something.'

She laughed again—a low, slightly husky laugh. 'So—aren't you going to say how shocked you are to see me here tonight?' she challenged. 'Not a week since poor Daddy's funeral, and here I am, gadding about town, enjoying myself.'

'Am I supposed to be shocked?'

'You expected it? Oh, dear!' She pouted prettily. 'I do so hate to be predictable.'

'There's little fear of that,' he assured her, a note of arid humour in his voice. 'Though I was sorry I wasn't able to attend the funeral—I was in Tokyo.'

'Pity. It was an excellent funeral.' Her soft mouth twisted into a wry smile. 'Daddy would have been delighted. Absolutely the correct degree of pomp and circumstance—even a bishop to do the honours! One of those distant cousins that only creep out of the woodwork at weddings and funerals. But I'm afraid I've upset all the old biddies now—my behaviour really is quite disgraceful, or so I've been told.'

One dark eyebrow arched in mocking question. 'Did you ever care what the old biddies thought?'

'Not in the least!' She shrugged her bare shoulders in a gesture of casual unconcern. She would never acknowledge, not even to herself, how much those censorious glances and whispered remarks had stung. Her relationship with her father had frequently been difficult, but she had adored him—old-fashioned, narrow-minded, obstinate curmudgeon that he was.

Oliver was perhaps one of the few who might understand that—his father and hers had been close friends since their own schooldays. But unfortunately Oliver Marsden was the last person with whom she could share her true feelings. Six years ago—prompted, she had suspected at the time, at least in part by the wishes of the two old men—he had proposed to her, and she had accepted. Predictably, it had ended in disaster.

Fortunately she had had to see little of him in the years since then—he had been working in New York, for some high-powered financial firm on Wall Street. But two months ago his father had announced that he was retiring as the chairman of Marsden Lambert, the small, traditional, family-owned investment bank, one of the few remaining independent banking houses in the City. And so Oliver had come home to take his place.

Which meant, inevitably, that they were going to run into each other rather more frequently. She really wasn't quite sure how she felt about that. On the few occasions they had met he had been perfectly civil, if a little distant, but she could never quite suppress a lingering sense of apprehension. Six years ago she had broken off their engagement on the very night it had been officially announced—and Oliver Marsden wasn't the man to easily forgive a thing like that.

But no trace of those troublesome thoughts were betrayed by her merrily dancing eyes as she fluttered her long lashes up at him in habitual flirtation. 'Anyway, they're probably right,' she acknowledged blithely. 'I'm afraid I really am irredeemably spoiled and selfish! Aren't you glad you didn't marry me after all?'

'You wouldn't have been spoiled if you'd married me.'

Ginny felt her heart thud sharply against her ribs; something in the grim humour of his voice warned her that he was only half joking. But she managed a laugh— though it had a forced sound even to her own ears. 'Ah, well, I'm glad I didn't marry you, then—I really rather like being spoiled...'

'Why, Ginny, dear—I didn't expect to see you here tonight.' Before Oliver could answer her sally, a soft, well-modulated voice that was all too familiar cut in on them. An ethereal Snow Queen, tall and willow-slim in a shimmering sheath of ice-white, a sparkling of silver frost dusted cleverly over the pale blonde hair that was drawn elegantly back from her fine-boned face, materialised at Oliver's side. Her smile was cool, assured, as she linked her hand confidently into his arm.

Oliver's stepsister: as fair as he was dark—and as beautiful as she was poisonous.

'Hello, Alina.' Not by a flicker did Ginny's smile diminish, nor her voice betray anything other than delight. 'Yes, I'm here. I just couldn't bear to miss the party!'

'I was so dreadfully upset when I heard about your father,' Alina purred with saccharine sympathy. 'It must have been such a dreadful shock for you.'

'Not really,' Ginny responded tautly. 'He'd been ill for quite a while.'

'Of course. And he was really quite old, wasn't he? But that dress is absolutely divine! I do think you're brave to wear a difficult colour like that.'

'Thank you.' Ginny was fairly sure there was some kind of spiteful dig in there somewhere, but she didn't have the will to retaliate right now. 'Well, it's been lovely speaking to you,' she murmured, slipping automatically into the classic formula for a polite escape. 'I'll catch you later, yes? Bye...'

And with a last brilliant smile she flitted away, plunging into her social role, sparkling with laughter, flirting with every male from eighteen to eighty—Ginny Hamilton the party-girl, in her element. Even tonight, with so many celebrities from the entertainment world as well as the cream of the aristocracy present, all eyes followed her wherever she moved around the crowded ballroom.

It wasn't that she was particularly beautiful—at least not in the classical sense. 'Striking' was the adjective most often used to describe her. Tall and lithely built, with a fall of hair as dark as polished ebony tumbling halfway down her back in vivid contrast to her clear ivory skin, and eyes of autumn green shaded by long, silken lashes. But her nose was a little too sharp for prettiness, her mouth a little too wide—as if, she was wont to say, her face hadn't all been put together on the same workbench.

Few people looked close enough to see the intelligence in those eyes, the determination in the set of her chin, the hint of vulnerability behind her generous smile. What they saw was exactly what she wanted them to see—the social butterfly, Daddy's spoiled little girl, frivolous and shallow. It was a quirky sort of pride that made her play to the very worst of the gossip about her, but she had learned a long time ago that it was a very effective disguise.

A few of those who watched her working her way around the room were vaguely aware that she had something to do with the committee that had organised tonight's event; only a handful knew that hers was the driving hand behind it. This was the real reason why she was here tonight, the reason she had forced herself to get dressed up in her finery and put on a show—though heaven knew it was the last thing she had felt like doing.

This was her forte. She had an almost magical talent for persuading people to dip their hands into their pockets for the many and varied charities to whom she lent her skills—she was inclined to say it was her only talent, though her many friends would have vigorously disagreed with her. No matter what the occasion, she was always able to make sure that people enjoyed themselves—and when they were enjoying themselves, they were more likely to be generous.

It didn't even have to be a charity they would normally have supported; tonight, for instance, it was for an organisation that ran hostels for homeless vagrants, many of them alcoholics and drug addicts—the sort that more than a few of the fine guests present would step over on their way to the opera, their noses wrinkled in distaste.

And she was certainly on form. Even the most disapproving of the old biddies couldn't remain impervious to her charm as she sympathised with them over the problem of finding a decent hairdresser who wouldn't charge the earth, and remembered the names of all their grandchildren, and which ones had been sickening with the measles. Only her very closest friends would have guessed how much effort it was costing her to keep that glittering façade in place.

It was an act she had perfected as a child. She had been just nine years old when her mother had died, but she had quickly learned how distressed her father was by her tears. So she had hidden them behind a sunny smile—and now it was second nature to her to keep up the pretence that everything was fine, no matter what emotions were tearing at her heart.

And it was an act that had stood her in good stead six years ago, when Alina's spite—and her own naïve pride—had brought all her romantic dreams crashing around her ears, and ended her engagement to Oliver.

The evening was going to be a success. Upwards of two hundred people were dancing beneath the magnificent chandeliers that swung from the high frescoed ceiling, their whirling reflections multiplied by the vast mirrors in their gilded frames that lined the whole of one wall. People seemed to enjoy wearing fancy dress—perhaps because it gave them a chance to leave their everyday lives behind and act out another role for a few hours.

Glancing around, Ginny felt a small glow of satisfaction. It had been worth the effort—it was as perfect as all the weeks of hard work and planning could make it, all the charm expended on persuading hard-headed businessmen to advertise in the glossily printed programme, the whirl of socialising as she'd taken every opportunity to persuade everyone in her wide ambit to buy a ticket.

So now she could snatch a few moments' respite. Deftly avoiding a rather portly Marie Antoinette—one of half a dozen—who was deeply absorbed in discovering the clues to the treasure hunt, she paused for a moment beside the heavy damask curtains that covered the tall French windows at the back of the ballroom. And then, when she was sure that no one was watching her, she melted through them and disappeared.

Outside was a small courtyard, bounded on all four sides by wings of the hotel; by day it would be a pleasant place to sit and drink coffee or eat ice-cream, but now it was deserted. She could still hear the music and laughter from the ballroom, but with the curtains drawn at the long windows it was quite private.

Though it was still only May, the evening air wasn't too chill. With a small sigh she perched on the edge of one of the tables, closing her eyes and massaging her temples with the tips of her fingers—her head was aching slightly from the effort of keeping her smile in place.

Maybe it was a foolish kind of pride that made her so determined to pretend that everything was going to be exactly the same as before her father had died—but then pride was about all she had left now. And they would find out soon enough, all those nasty gossips who were always so eager to pass judgement on her. No doubt they would say she had got her rightful comeuppance.

Of course, she shouldn't really complain—it was her own fault that she was the target of so much critical attention. She had created a scandal the night she had broken off her engagement to Oliver, and she had done nothing since to redeem her reputation. Not that anyone would believe her if she tried to protest the truth. And anyway she didn't want to; the lies were a perfect disguise for the hurt inside—a hurt that she realised now had never really gone away.

It had probably been a little reckless of her to provoke Oliver with that flippant remark, she mused wryly. She had intended it to suggest that the past was forgotten, buried history, all the scars long-healed—but the glint in those dark eyes had warned her that he didn't quite see it that way.

She had long suspected that, of course. Even at nineteen she had sensed that the smooth, urbane veneer he presented to the world hid a rather more dangerous creature—just as beneath that immaculately tailored dinner jacket he wore tonight there was a lean, hard-muscled male body, more suited to an athlete or road-digger than the chairman of one of the City's oldest and most respected investment banks.

What would they make of him in Threadneedle Street? And, perhaps more interestingly, what would he make of them? Marsden Lambert—the Lamberts were long-gone now, though their name remained on the masthead—had the reputation of being one of the most stuffy, traditional, ultra-conservative institutions in the Square Mile. Now that Oliver was at the helm, she couldn't see it staying that way for long. In New York he had been in the business of futures arbitrage—a game that so far as she could see was little removed from straightforward gambling. And he had been very successful at it. It could be worth watching the sky for fireworks.

And now that he was back in London, what was it going to mean for her? To be honest, it was probably just as well that they hadn't got married six years ago, she reflected—she was wise enough now to recognise that what she had been so sure was love had probably been no more than an adolescent infatuation. And he would very quickly have got bored with a naïve little bride, wrapped up in cotton wool by her doting father, her head full of foolish romantic notions culled from the pages of glossy magazines.

But though he would certainly have recognised that himself by now, she couldn't be sure that he wouldn't still find some way of punishing her for what she had done. While her father was alive, she had felt safe—Oliver would never have done anything that might distress his father's oldest friend. But now her father was gone...? Those dark eyes had conveyed an unmistakable hint of warning. Was the polite truce that had existed between them finally coming to an end...?

'Hi. I thought I might find you out here. Taking a breather?'

Ginny glanced over her shoulder, greeting her best friend Sara with a wry smile. 'A bit,' she conceded. 'I found I couldn't quite take all those disapproving stares, after all. Everyone thinks I'm a heartless bitch for even being here, don't they?'

'Well... Some do, perhaps,' Sara admitted reluctantly. 'The ones who don't know you.'

Ginny chuckled with laughter. 'Another smudge on my reputation! I must be beyond redemption by now.'

'Don't be silly,' Sara protested. 'It's all just a lot of stupid, idle gossip.'

'Ah, but there's no smoke without fire!' Ginny insisted, her eyes dancing.

Sara snorted in disgust. 'It's your own fault—you positively encourage it.'

Ginny acknowledged the point with a wicked smile. 'Of course. It's so much more fun being thought a scarlet woman than a little goody two-shoes!'

Sara laughed with her, but she wasn't so easily fooled. 'You didn't need to come tonight, you know,' she said gently. 'We could have managed.'

Ginny shook her head, suddenly serious. 'No... No, I couldn't leave it all to you. Besides, what's the point of sitting at home moping? It won't bring him back.' She hesitated, her soft mouth quirked into a crooked smile. 'Anyway,' she added wistfully, 'this may be the last swanky party I ever go to.'

Sara returned her a look of startled question. 'What on earth do you mean?'

Ginny lifted her eyes to gaze up at the high, cold stars; when her mother had died, she'd always used to imagine her as a star, up there in the sky, always watching over her. Was her father there too now? Somewhere the two of them together...? 'Remember that big insurance syndicate that crashed a few years ago, leaving people owing ludicrous amounts of money? Well, Dad was one of the Names.'

Her friend's eyes widened. 'Oh... Lord!'

'Exactly.' She couldn't quite keep the trace of bitterness from her voice. 'It's ironic really. He was always so conservative about money—he would never have even looked at anything he didn't think was utterly safe and respectable. But apparently this syndicate is having to pay out claims on several major environmental disasters—they won't even know for years exactly how much it will come to.'

'But that's dreadful!' Sara protested. 'Isn't there anything you can do?'

'Not a thing!' Absently Ginny traced the edge of one of the paving stones with her foot. 'I just wish he'd told me. Not that there was much I could have done, I suppose, but I can't help feeling guilty for all the money I've spent on clothes and frippery, while he was struggling to meet their demands. He just went on paying my allowance as if nothing had happened.'

Sara shook her head. 'He probably didn't want you to worry.'

'I know. Can't you just hear him? ''Now, don't you go bothering your pretty little head about it.'' Unfortunately, I can do nothing else *but* worry at the moment. I'm going to have to sell the house.'

'Oh, no!' Sara's blue eyes were moist with sympathy. 'But that's terrible! Where are you supposed to live?'

Ginny shrugged her slim shoulders, refusing to let the despair engulf her. 'Oh, I'll find somewhere.'

'You could...come and live with us,' Sara offered diffidently. 'There's plenty of room.'

Ginny shook her head, laughing. 'I'm afraid Buckingham Palace wouldn't be big enough for Peter and me. How on earth did you ever come to marry my blockish cousin? I've always thought it was my fault for introducing you to him.'

Sara gurgled, taking the teasing in good part. 'He isn't really blockish,' she protested. 'Just a little...cautious at times. But seriously, what will you do? How will you manage?'

'I suppose I shall have to get a job or something,' Ginny mused dismally. 'The trouble is, I'm really not qualified for anything. Poor old Daddy—he had the most antiquated ideas about women and careers. And I suppose I was lazy enough to go along with it.'

'It wasn't laziness,' Sara argued, indignant on her friend's behalf. 'You didn't want to upset him, not with his heart condition.'

'Well...yes,' Ginny conceded. 'But the result is that I've got no qualifications—unless you count my diploma from the Ecole de Cuisine. The only thing I can usefully do is arrange this kind of thing...' She waved her hand in the direction of the crowded ballroom.

'And you're brilliant at it!' Sara asserted with enthusiasm. 'Maybe you could make a career out of that? A lot of charities employ professional fundraisers these days.'

Ginny shook her head, her smile grim. 'The only reason I can get all these people to come along is because I move in the right circles. How long do you think I could keep it up if I was poor?'

'Well, you could always marry a millionaire,' Sara giggled. 'There's lots in there to choose from—I don't suppose you'd have the least difficulty.'

Abruptly Ginny snapped her fingers. 'That's it! Sara, you're brilliant.'

Her friend stared at her, aghast. 'I was only joking,' she protested.

'*I* wasn't,' Ginny declared firmly. 'It's the perfect solution. If I marry someone rich enough, not only might I be able to keep the house, but no one else will ever have to find out that poor Daddy ended his life worse than bankrupt. He was so proud, bless him—he didn't want anyone to know. The least I can do is go on keeping his secret for him. Now, come on,' she urged. 'Who do we know that would do? What about Jeremy? He's quite good-looking—and nice with it.'

'Oh, no—he's too nice,' Sara argued, laughing a little uncertainly. 'You'd trample all over him.'

'Hmm... You could be right,' Ginny acknowledged, her head on one side as she gave the point her serious consideration. 'Okay... Ralph, then?'

Sara wrinkled her nose. 'He always smells of horses.'

'So? I like horses. Though I suppose it could get a bit much all the time. Alastair?'

'You've always said he's got big ears.'

'Well, that doesn't mean he couldn't be a perfectly good husband,' Ginny pointed out fairly. 'Let's put him first on the list.'

'It's a pity you split up with Oliver,' Sara remarked, tipping her head to one side. 'He's *very* rich—and good-looking with it.'

'Oliver?' Ginny managed a careless laugh. 'Oh, no—he's much too arrogant! I wouldn't marry him if I was desperate.'

'I thought you were desperate?'

'I am.' Ginny admitted, airily dismissive. 'And I still wouldn't marry him! Ah, it sounds as if they're ready to serve supper.' She seized with relief on the excuse to prevent her friend from probing that topic any deeper. 'Let's go in.'

The ballroom was clearing rapidly as everyone drifted through into the supper room. Ginny had glanced in earlier in the evening, and it had been quite evident that the head waiter had everything well under control. The tables looked wonderful, each with a centrepiece of delicate freesias, the light of the chandeliers sparkling on the crystal and silverware laid out on tablecloths of crisp white Irish linen.

'Ah, there's our table!' Sara declared, taking Ginny's hand and making a beeline across the room.

As she followed her, Ginny cursed quietly to herself. Damn—she should have checked the table allocations. She might have guessed that if it was left to Peter he would sign up to sit with Oliver—just because they had once rowed pairs together at university, anyone would think they were blood brothers!

With the ease of long practice she summoned a smile to her lips. 'Good evening again!' she greeted him lightly as she swept up to the table, gracefully swaying her wide crinoline skirt between Julius Caesar, who was looking for his own table, and a stuffed sheep that had been temporarily laid aside by its Bo-Peep. 'You're with us for supper?'

'If there are no objections?' he queried, softly mocking.

One finely drawn eyebrow arched in an affectation of surprise that he should even think it. 'Not from me. Ah, thank you,' she added as he smoothly drew out her chair for her, pre-empting Jeremy, who was nominally her date for the evening.

Poor Jeremy, clumsy and confused, dropped the hand that had been reaching for the chair, and with an expression of disappointment on his handsome, boyish face sat down beside her. She compensated him with her warmest smile—which brought a slightly startled look to his face. Yes, Sara was probably right, Ginny mused wryly—it really wouldn't be fair to persuade him to marry her, although he was probably the easiest target. He was just so eager to please—he'd drive her crazy inside of a week.

Another couple had come to join them, also old friends of Peter and Oliver's, taking up the remaining seats at the table. Lucy, resplendent as a flamenco dancer, complete with a slightly lopsided *mantilla,* plopped herself quickly down in the seat next to Oliver's, patting it invitingly. 'Oliver, sweetie! Come and sit down!' she coaxed, her slightly over-loud voice betraying the fact that she had already been hitting the sherry. 'Why have you stayed away from London for so long, you naughty boy? We don't have enough good-looking men!'

Oliver smiled, the perfect gentleman. 'I'm sorry—if I had realised my absence would be noticed I would have come back sooner,' he responded easily.

Lucy hooted with laughter. 'So tell me, how was New York? I just love it there, you know. It's so exciting!

And you can't beat Macy's for shopping. I go every year—I do my Christmas shopping there. Have you ever been?' she asked, smiling benignly across the table at Ginny.

'Once,' she responded tautly, careful not to let her eyes stray towards Oliver.

'Ah, yes,' Alina put in, her voice honeyed. 'It was a pity it was such a brief visit. You really can't enjoy everything New York has to offer in just a few days.'

The hint was so subtle it could easily have been missed. But there was no way Ginny could have forgotten that Alina also had spent a great deal of time in New York—nor did she fail to notice the sly flicker of those ice-blue eyes in Oliver's direction.

Fortunately Lucy's husband Nigel innocently turned the conversation with a remark about the current state of the Dow-Jones index, and as the men launched into a discussion of international finance Ginny was able to take a few minutes to talk herself back into a state of reasonable composure.

She was also able to study Oliver covertly from beneath her lashes. The past six years seemed to have left barely a mark on him—if anything he was better looking now than he had been in his twenties. There was a hardness of maturity about him, etched into those angular cheekbones, drawn in the line of that mouth that she had always found so fascinating. She could still remember the first time he had kissed her...

A dark glint of mockery stabbing across the table warned her that he had caught her watching him. With a lazy deliberation he let her see that he was subjecting her to the same kind of scrutiny, letting his gaze drift down over the slender curve of her throat to linger almost insolently on the firm ripeness of her breasts, his slow smile registering approval.

An odd little frisson of heat shivered down her spine. Six years ago she had still been a skinny, gangling teenager, with no curves to speak of—she could never have worn a dress like this. Beneath his gaze she could feel a warm blush spreading up through her body, but she refused to give him the satisfaction of looking away, forcing herself instead to return him a cool smile.

Jeremy was filling her glass with wine, and she took up her fork, relieved to be able to focus her attention on her plate. But though the food was delicious, each course designed to be as much a feast for the eye as the taste-buds, her usually healthy appetite seemed to have strangely deserted her. As the main course came and went—tender slices of venison in a piquant redcurrant sauce—she realised that she had eaten even less than Alina, who always ate like a sparrow, intent on keeping that reed-thin figure.

Against her will, her eyes were drawn back across the table, watching from beneath her lashes as the slender blonde leaned close to Oliver, murmuring something to him that was obviously too private for the hearing of the general *hoi polloi* around the table...

Dammit, there it was again, that same old bitter amalgam of anger and resentment and jealousy. Surely she should have got over all that by now? It had been more than six years. At nineteen, unsure of herself, unsure of Oliver, she had been an easy victim for the clever older woman. But she was older herself now, and hopefully wiser—she ought to be more of an equal match.

The arrival of coffee and port was the signal for the highlight of the evening to commence. A small ripple of anticipation ran round the room as everyone sought their programmes among the debris of the supper.

'Darling, this is an absolutely super idea!' A somewhat over-aged Miss Muffett, complete with a gruesomely hairy spider on a stick, paused beside their table on her way to powder her nose. 'I'm so excited—I don't know which lot to bid for!'

'Then bid for them all, Lady Lulworth,' Ginny suggested with a smile. 'The more people bidding, the more it will drive the prices up.'

'Oh—yes, of course! Oh, I will, then—I'll bid for them all. After all, it's all in a good cause, isn't it?'

Ginny's eyes were dancing as she turned back to her companions. 'She hasn't a clue what it's for,' she chuckled merrily.

The others laughed, but Peter was frowning. 'I'm really not sure this is in terribly good taste, you know,' he murmured, leaning towards Ginny. 'Particularly for you to stand as one of the prizes.'

'Oh, don't be stuffy!' she retorted. 'It's just a bit of fun.'

'I just don't much care for it, that's all,' he grumbled.

'Hush!' Sara chided him. 'They're about to start the bidding.'

This was Ginny's secret triumph; it had cost her a considerable amount of effort and outlay of charm, but she had managed to persuade a dozen or so of her friends and acquaintances to offer not just their money but also their time. Each was to be a 'Slave for a Day,' putting their own special skills or resources at the disposal of the highest bidder.

The first 'Slave' was another of her oldest friends, who was famous for her flower arrangements; her offer to fill the home of the winner with flowers proved extremely popular. The bidding was vigorous, and Ginny sat with her fingers tightly crossed; every penny raised would go straight to the charity.

It had been a real stroke of luck that she had been able to recruit the services of Cornell Elliot, the popular comedian, to be the auctioneer. He had the audience in stitches with a series of quick-fire impersonations—an apparently off-the-cuff performance that Ginny knew he had rehearsed in as much detail as if he was being paid for it. The next three lots went as well as the first, Cornell bantering with the audience and encouraging the good-natured competition, running up the bids in a very satisfying fashion.

'Ah, now—ooh, no, really! This one's going to be *very* popular—especially with the ladies. Where's my wife? Sit on your hands, dear—you can't have this one. Oliver Marsden—where are you, Oliver? Ah…!'

Like the other 'slaves', Oliver rose briefly to his feet, acknowledging the applause with a slight bow.

'How about this, then? Oliver is offering to fly the highest bidder to Paris in his private plane, for a candlelit dinner on the Seine! Come along, ladies,' he added wickedly. 'This has got to be an offer you can't refuse. Who's going to open the bidding? Ah, thank you, madam.'

The bids came thick and fast, as Cornell whipped up the enthusiasm. Oliver sat smiling quietly, his eyes flickering around the room as he watched who was bidding. Beside him, Alina wore a small smile of satisfaction, as if the price being offered reflected well on her. There were times, Ginny reflected with a touch of wicked humour, when she wished she was still ten years old, and a well-aimed dollop of raspberry sorbet could have appropriately expressed her feelings.

Lady Lulworth was bidding excitedly, squeaking with agitation as she waved her unfortunate spider in the air to attract Cornell's attention, howling with disappointment every time her bid was topped.

'The bid is against you, Lady Lulworth,' Cornell advised, teasing her to bid again. 'Are you going to raise?'

'Oh...! Oh, dear... I...'

Cornell raised his gavel. 'Going for the first time...'

'Yes! Yes—another fifty pounds! My bid, my bid!'

'Regretting making the offer, Oliver?' Ginny teased quietly.

'Not at all,' Oliver responded with mild amusement.

'She'll foist that daughter of hers onto you,' Jeremy warned. 'She's been desperate to get her married off for years!'

'Do I have any more bids?' Cornell was asking. 'Going for the first time... Going for the second time...' He paused for dramatic effect, as Lady Lulworth bounced up and down in her seat. 'Sold to the lady with the spider.'

'Oh, wonderful!' She jumped up, rushing to throw her arms around Cornell and smack a kiss on his cheek, and then to Oliver. 'Oh, I shall be looking forward to it so much!' she babbled, clasping her hands. 'I can hardly wait.'

'I hope you'll enjoy it,' he responded genially.

'Oh, I'm sure I shall. I'm quite sure I shall!'

'Sounds ominous,' warned Jeremy darkly as the good lady at last returned to her own table. 'Watch out for the daughter! Dreadful girl! Nearly got her claws into Edward Chatsby last year, you know—had him looking at engagement rings. Only just got out in time. Still, don't suppose you need the warning, eh? Must be pretty sharp at steering clear of the old parson's mousetrap by now... Oh...' He stopped himself abruptly, suddenly colouring as he realised that his gabbling had led him into committing an embarrassing *faux pas*. 'Oh, dear... I'm sorry... I forgot... I mean, about you two...'

Ginny felt a tightness constricting her chest, but somehow managed a merry laugh. 'Oh, don't worry about that, Jerry. It was all a very long time ago. We...can both look back on it now and laugh—can't we, Oliver?'

He returned the smile, perfectly civilised and polite— was it just her overheated imagination that seemed to read a glint of menace in his eyes? 'Of course,' he responded, raising his wine glass to his lips. 'It would be really rather foolish for either of us to harbour any...antagonism about it.'

Her mouth dry, Ginny reached for her own wine glass. Suddenly it seemed awfully hot in the ballroom. She fanned herself with her programme, but it didn't seem to help.

With the audience now thoroughly warmed to the idea of the auction, bidding continued at a lively pace for the remaining lots. Ginny was mentally totting up the total, her satisfaction growing as they reached and passed even her most optimistic estimate. It really did make it all worthwhile.

At last Cornell announced, 'And so, ladies and gentlemen, we come to our final lot of the evening—and this one's going to be the most popular of all, I'm quite sure. Our very own Ginny! Come along, sweetheart—take a bow.'

Laughing, Ginny rose to her feet, essaying a graceful curtsey in response to the applause.

'Ginny's offering her unique talent for arranging parties to whoever bids the highest. From invitations right through to the washing up! So, who's going to open the bidding for me?'

The bidding was lively, aided by Ginny, who laughingly encouraged it upwards with her hands. It quickly topped all the other prices and was still rising; the top bid was from a nice couple that she had known for many years—their daughter was getting engaged soon, and she suspected that was why they were so keen to win her services.

'Six hundred pounds, I'm bid!' Cornell enthused. 'Do I have any advance on that?' He lifted his gavel to crack it down. 'For the first time...'

Suddenly a laconic voice spoke from her own table. 'One thousand pounds.'

A ripple of surprise ran round the room—partly because of the amount of money being bid, but also because of who was doing the bidding. Oliver. Ginny felt a treacherous blush of pink colour her cheeks as she stared into those level dark eyes. Why was he doing this?

Quickly she glanced back to Douglas and Marjorie, pleading. But reluctantly Douglas shook his head. 'Sorry—we're out,' he said.

Every eye in the room turned back to Oliver as Cornell lifted his gavel. 'Any advance on one thousand pounds?' he queried doubtfully. 'For the first time... For the second time...' The clack of his gavel seemed to strike a sharp pain into Ginny's heart. 'Sold to Oliver Marsden.'

CHAPTER TWO

IT WAS late in the evening. The auction, which had raised a quite magnificent sum for the charity, was over; some people had left, but others seemed intent on dancing till dawn. Ginny at last began to feel that she could relax, and leave the rest of the evening to take care of itself. Slipping discreetly through the French window again, out to the secluded courtyard, she drew in a long, deep breath of the cool night air, closing her eyes and massaging her temples with her fingertips to ease away the strain of the evening.

Damn Oliver Marsden! Why on earth had he bid for her so outrageously? He might have known it would create an unwelcome stir of interest, reminding people of that ill-starred engagement six years ago. Six years...! Was it really as long as that? Sometimes it seemed as if it was only yesterday—and sometimes it seemed like a lifetime.

The memories that she had kept locked away for so long were spinning around her, drawing her back in time...back to a sunny day in May when she was almost eighteen. That, for her, had been the beginning, though she hadn't really been aware of it at the time. That was the day that the first coils had begun to tangle around her heart.

As a favour to her father, Oliver had come to pick her up from school for the half-term holiday. The sixth form common room had happened to overlook the drive, and the moment his car had swept through the main gates a buzz of excitement stirred the room...

* * *

'Hey! Get the wheels!'

'Classic!'

A dozen nubile teenagers crowded the window seats, straining to catch a glimpse of the new arrival. The car was certainly something—a sleek, long-nosed Aston Martin, its twin superchargers rumbling like a pair of caged lions beneath the muscular bonnet, its dark green bodywork gleaming in the sun. But as it drew to a halt, and a tall, dark-haired figure swung from behind the wheel, the excitement hit an altogether different pitch.

'Never mind the wheels—get the guy!'

'Mm-mm! He could have the last potato off my plate any time!'

'Who is he?' the demand went up. 'Who's he come to meet?'

Ginny gazed down out of the window, slightly perplexed. She had known Oliver Marsden all her life, but until this moment he had made little impact on her consciousness. After all, he was nearly ten years older than her, and while she had been growing up he had mostly been away from home—at school or university, or more recently in New York, working for some dull old bank.

Was he really that attractive? She had never really thought about it—but her friends certainly seemed to think so. Which meant that there was a very definite kudos in being connected with him. So she stepped away from the window, affecting an air of casual unconcern. 'Oh, it's just Oliver,' she drawled. 'He's...sort of my brother.'

'What do you mean, "sort of" your brother?' Laurel Kennedy protested, puzzled. 'You haven't got a brother.'

'Well, his father is my godfather, and my father's his godfather,' Ginny explained with somewhat convoluted logic. 'I suppose he is quite fanciable, but then I've known him for ever. Anyway, I must dash,' she added, swinging her bag casually onto her shoulder. 'He does hate to be kept hanging around.'

Halfway down the stairs she paused, and, glancing swiftly around to make sure that no one was watching, she fumbled impatiently in her bag and found a hair-brush to drag through her long hair, cursing the school rule that strictly banned make-up. Then, turning the waistband of her skirt over to shorten the hem, she swung her bag over her shoulder again and strolled languidly out to where Oliver was exercising his considerable charm on the formidable Miss Danvers, the deputy headmistress.

'Ah, Virginia, there you are.' Miss Danvers' manner was almost girlish. 'Well, run along, dear, and have a nice break. Drive safely.'

'I will,' Oliver assured her genially. 'Jump in, Gin.'

Ginny favoured him with what she hoped was an alluring and enigmatic smile, walking with graceful dignity round to the passenger door, which he had leaned across to open as he slid back behind the wheel. He slanted her a look of mild amusement as he turned the key in the ignition and the well-tuned engine purred into life.

'Got a lot of homework?' he enquired, glancing at her bulging sports-bag.

'A little,' she conceded, irritated that he should have drawn attention to her schoolgirl status when she was trying to appear grown-up.

'Well, let's get you home then,' he responded, a sardonic inflection in his voice. 'The sooner you start it, the sooner you'll get it finished, and then you can relax and start working on your suntan.'

'I don't sunbathe,' she informed him coolly. 'It ages your skin.'

She posed herself as elegantly as she could in her seat,

her hair sleek around her shoulders, her coltish legs crossed, savouring the thought of the envious eyes watching her from the tall Georgian windows of the common room as the car swept through the main gates and onto the road for London.

It must have been a couple of years since she had last seen him, she mused, studying him covertly from beneath her lashes. He didn't look much like a banker—at least, she'd never seen a banker with a pair of shoulders like that, wide and hard beneath his cool white cotton shirt. And he didn't have banker's hands, either—soft and podgy and effete. His hands were strong, effortlessly controlling the powerful car, but sensitive too, responsive to every movement of the steering wheel...

An odd little shimmer of heat ran through her, and she looked away quickly, startled by the way her heart had suddenly begun to beat a little faster.

He glanced across at her, that intriguing mouth curved into a laconic smile. 'Is it too warm for you?' he enquired, impeccably polite. 'I can turn the air-conditioning up if you like.'

'Oh... No, it's okay, thanks.'

'Some music?'

She nodded, and he flicked a switch, filling the car with the notes of a smoky jazz clarinet that sounded as if it had been marinated in spilled whisky. She had never heard anything quite like it before, but as it swirled around her, seeping into her brain, it seemed to conjure images that heated her blood and made her heartbeat accelerate again.

But it wasn't just the music that gave the odd effect, she realised with a faint hint of surprise—it was the man beside her at the wheel of the car. Strange—she had been out with plenty of boys, but she had never known herself

to react like this before. But then...they had been just
boys. Oliver Marsden was a man—mature, experi-
enced...

What would it be like if he kissed her? She slid another secret glance towards him, studying that faintly
arrogant profile. His mouth was firm, with just a hint of
controlled fullness about the lower lip. She could imagine that when he was angry it would look positively
hard. But when he smiled there was an intriguing hint
of sensuality about it...

The music ended, and the CD player clicked off.
Ginny tipped her head on one side, drawing in a careful
breath to steady her voice to speak. 'That was good,'
she remarked, trying to sound as if she knew her New
Orleans from her Charlie Parker.

He quirked one eyebrow towards her. 'You liked it?
I thought most girls of your age were into some bunch
of hairy Neanderthals with one-note guitars.'

'I'm not most girls,' she responded, stung.

'Aren't you?' That fascinating mouth curved into a
smile of lazy amusement. 'I shall try to remember that.'

Dammit—he was *laughing* at her! Her eyes sparked
with angry indignation, and, turning her head sharply
away, she stared out at the passing countryside, point-
edly ignoring him.

The silence stretched awkwardly between them...at
least it was awkward on her part—if Oliver was even
aware of it, he gave no sign. If only she could think of
something scintillatingly witty to say to impress him...
Although unfortunately he knew to the day how old she
was, and it wasn't very likely that he was going to be
much impressed by a kid of seventeen.

The beautiful car ate up the miles, and much too soon
they had turned off the main road and into the village.
She could see the straight Victorian chimneys and dor-
mer roofs of Thornton Lodge above the trees. Oliver

turned the car in through the tall gates, and the tyres crunched on the neatly kept gravel of the front drive as it rolled gently to a halt.

With a sharp stab of frustration Ginny realised that any chance she might have had of dazzling him with her intelligence and personality was gone. Okay, so maybe he wouldn't have been so easily captivated as a boy of her own age, but she could at least have *tried*. Instead she had wasted the whole journey being stupidly tongue-tied—Oliver must think her the most boring female he had ever encountered!

Furious with herself for her own uncharacteristic awkwardness, she could think only of getting away as quickly as she could. Snatching up her school-bag, she stumbled out of the car, getting her foot caught in her seat-belt and almost ending up in an undignified heap on the ground. She straightened, her eyes glaring a frosty challenge—let him just dare to laugh again...!

But he wasn't laughing—he was smiling. And the impact of that unbridled sensuality took her breath away. 'I...er...thank you for the lift,' she blurted out somehow.

'My pleasure.' He leaned across and closed the door, just a hint of sardonic amusement in his eyes to warn her that he knew perfectly well why she was standing there on the drive like some kind of moron, and then he gunned the engine and swung the car neatly around her, leaving barely a graze on the gravel as it cruised back down the drive and out of the gates.

Ginny had more than a year to regret the wasted opportunity; Oliver went back to New York. To be honest, she didn't really think about him that much; there was just a lingering image in the back of her mind, of which she was barely aware—a kind of benchmark against which she was subconsciously comparing all the boys who seemed to want to take her light-hearted flirtatiousness as encouragement. Inevitably, none of them could match up.

Besides, she had other things to think about. In spite of all her teachers' dire predictions, she left school with three reasonably good 'A' levels, but she really didn't have much idea what sort of career she wanted to take up. And when she had broached the topic with her father, he had been airily dismissive.

'What do you want to bother your head with things like that for?' he had demanded. 'You don't need to think about a job. Besides, you'll just be getting married. Waste of time.'

She privately had some reservations about the getting married bit, but, lacking any clear ambitions, she hadn't really argued with him as much as she might. Besides, she was concerned about his health—his doctor had recently diagnosed his 'indigestion' as angina, and she was anxious not to upset him. To stave off the boredom of being a lady of leisure she enrolled in a Cordon Bleu cookery course, but it had never seemed like her lifetime's vocation.

It was the night of her nineteenth birthday party when she saw Oliver again. She hadn't known that he would even be at home, so she was more than a little surprised when, crossing the hall some time in the middle of the evening, she glanced towards the front door to see him arriving with his father and stepmother.

Suddenly that image that had been locked in her mind lurched into sharp relief, and she realised why all those callow boys had seemed so inadequate. She drew in a sharp breath, struggling to control the alarming acceleration of her heartbeat. 'Uncle Howard—Aunt Margot!' she cried, darting forward. 'How lovely to see you. Thank you for coming.'

'Why, Virginia, my dear.' Her godfather, like her father, always refused to use the shorter version of her name. He leaned over to peck her on the cheek. 'Happy Birthday. And looking so grown-up! Isn't she, Oliver?'

Those dark eyes met hers with a flicker of amused appreciation as they slid down over her slender silhouette. She had chosen to wear trousers—slim cut, in a liquid gunmetal-grey silk—teamed with a matching sleeveless top that had a softly draped neckline. She knew that it flattered her colouring, and her slender height—she didn't suit the kind of floral, frilly frocks that were all the current rage.

'Very grown-up,' Oliver responded to his father's comment. 'Happy Birthday, Ginny.'

To her chagrin, she felt a blush of deep pink creep up over her cheeks, but she managed to return him what she hoped was a cool smile; if he thought he could patronise her now, as he had before, he would find that he was very much mistaken. She was no longer a naïve little schoolgirl.

'Thank you,' she responded with dignity. 'Please come in. Can I get you a drink?'

'I'll have a Scotch, please.'

'With soda, or just ice?' she enquired politely.

He quirked one dark eyebrow in faintly mocking amusement, shaking his head. 'With Scotch? Oh, no—you never water down a good Scotch,' he instructed her softly.

'Oh...' Her heart had started to beat rather faster than usual, and she couldn't quite make herself meet his eyes. Confused at her own unaccustomed shyness, she made her escape as quickly as she could, cravenly sending one of the waiters her father had hired with the caterers to take his drink.

The party was in full swing, and everyone seemed to

be enjoying themselves, but Ginny kept herself busy—playing the perfect hostess, making sure that she spoke to everyone, introducing those who didn't know each other, drawing the quieter ones to join in the conversation—Mademoiselle Brissot, who had taught deportment at school, would have been proud of her. But all the time she could see Oliver out of the corner of her eye, though she was careful not to let him see her watching him, or to get too close.

She was handing round a tray of canapés when he suddenly appeared at her side. 'My father tells me I should try one of these,' he remarked, helping himself to one of the dainty parcels of filo pastry, stuffed with avocado and sun-dried tomatoes. 'Made by your own fair hand, I understand?'

'Oh... Yes, that's right,' she managed to respond, struggling for a lightness of tone. 'Though actually I cheated—the pastry was frozen.'

He smiled. 'You shouldn't have told me that—I wouldn't have guessed. So you're training to be a Cordon Bleu chef then?'

'That sounds a bit grand for it,' she returned, fleetingly surprised that she had apparently been a topic of conversation in the Marsden household. 'But I've learned all sorts of useful things—like which wine to serve with roast pheasant, and how to peel asparagus.'

'You never quite know when that sort of information might come in handy.'

Her eyes sparkled with merriment. 'That's true. If I'm ever caught in a lifeboat, and have to convince them not to throw me overboard, I can say, "Not me—I know how to peel asparagus." It could save my life!'

He laughed with genuine humour, and she felt a warm little glow inside her that she had actually succeeded in amusing him. But for some crazy reason that very fact made her feel suddenly awkward, and she moved to step past him. 'Well, if you'll excuse me, I...have to circulate...'

'You've been circulating all evening.' With a decisive movement he took the canapé tray from her and set it down on a nearby table. 'It's your birthday—come and have a dance.'

He had taken her hand in his, and suddenly she felt so dizzy she was afraid she was going to faint. A marquee had been erected in the garden, and most of the younger guests were dancing to the music of a three-piece band—local amateurs, but really quite good. She felt herself stiffen slightly as he drew her onto the dance-floor, and into his arms—she could only hope that if he noticed the slight blush of pink in her cheeks he would assume that it was due to the heat.

But Mademoiselle's excellent training stood her in good stead, and she managed to lift her eyes to meet his, smiling brightly. 'I didn't know you were coming home,' she remarked in a pleasantly conversational tone. 'Pops never mentioned it.'

That beguiling mouth curved into a dry smile. *'Pops?'* he repeated, one eyebrow arched in quizzical amusement. 'Does Uncle James know you call him that?'

She shrugged her slim shoulders in a gesture of casual dismissal, furious with herself for letting slip the adolescent sobriquet. 'He...doesn't mind,' she countered awkwardly.

His sardonic laughter conveyed his doubt. 'I came home on Thursday,' he told her in answer to her question. 'Just a business trip, I'm afraid—I was fortunate to have this opportunity to mix it with a little pleasure.'

He was smiling down at her, and she had to struggle against the feeling that she was drowning in the liquid darkness of his eyes. 'What's…New York like?' she asked, not quite able to keep her voice steady.

'Fast, noisy, crowded… It's great, if you can take the pace. There's always something going on, and you can always find a bar open or a place to eat, any time of the day or night. You'll have to come across for a visit some time.'

'Oh…yes… That would be…fun,' she responded a little breathlessly. Of course he was just being polite—he didn't really mean it.

But as she danced in his arms, it seemed as if any kind of foolish dream could come true. It was so crowded that they had to dance quite close together, just moving to the rhythm, their feet shifting on the wood-block flooring that had been laid over the lawn, their bodies occasionally brushing against each other.

She was startlingly aware of him, of a hint of raw maleness that was quite outside her experience; he had taken off his jacket, and his tie, and unfastened the collar of his crisp white shirt, and in the shadow at the base of his throat she could see a smattering of rough, dark curling hair. And there were muscles—hard, toned muscles—beneath that pristine white cotton, and a subtle scent on his skin—not an aftershave, she was sure, but an evocative muskiness that was all his own.

It was like being drugged. Strange, disturbing images were swirling in her brain, and as he drew her a little closer against him she was very much afraid that he would be aware of the racing beat of her heart. The song ended, and another one began, but they continued dancing. Ginny had closed her eyes, losing herself in a fantasy that she knew was as dangerous as it was enticing. Nothing was real except the music, and his arms around her…

'Okay...um...that's it for now. We're...um...gonna take a break. Back in...um...half an hour or so.'

The semi-coherent mumble from the singer broke the spell. Ginny drew back, reluctant to return to reality, afraid that if she lifted her eyes to Oliver's he would read in them all her foolish dreams. But he put one finger beneath her chin, tilting up her face to his, and as he smiled down at her there was no trace of the mockery that had characterised his previous attitude towards her.

The marquee had cleared rapidly as everyone made a rush for the bar, leaving them alone except for a last one or two who seemed to be taking little notice of them.

'I'm afraid I have to leave now,' Oliver said softly. 'I have some very boring meetings to attend tomorrow, and some very boring reports to read tonight.' His thumb brushed lightly across her trembling lips, and then he bent his head, his breath warm against her cheek, his mouth thrillingly firm and sensuous on hers. 'Goodnight, sweet little Virginia,' he murmured. 'Don't break too many hearts.'

The last thing Ginny expected was that anything would come of Oliver's casual invitation to visit New York—she had been quite sure that he would instantly forget all about it.

It had been her father's suggestion; he had offered her the trip as a reward for passing her diploma—which had surprised her a little, since he had never taken a great deal of interest in her educational achievements. Watching the wide expanse of the blue-grey Atlantic, sliding away below her, she smiled wryly to herself. She had a very uncomfortable suspicion that he and Uncle Howard had cooked up some kind of scheme between them—and she wasn't at all sure how Oliver would welcome having her foisted on him for a whole week.

But as the seat-belt light came on, and the huge 747 banked and began its long descent into Kennedy Airport, excitement displaced any other thoughts from her mind. New York! She would enjoy the trip, anyway, no matter how Oliver behaved towards her.

Her doubts returned as she manoeuvred her way through Customs. Her father had said that Oliver would be there to meet her, but for a daunting moment the vast, crowded arrivals hall was just a sea of anonymous faces. And then she saw him, his dark head a little higher than those around him, and instantly her heartbeat started to play a crazy rumba beneath her ribs.

He cut through the crowd towards her, greeting her with that familiar faintly mocking smile as he took her suitcase, lifting its weight with no apparent effort. 'Hi. Have a good flight?' he queried in a friendly enough tone.

'Oh... Yes, fine, thank you,' she responded, trying hard to hold onto some semblance of poise. She had been dreaming about him ever since the night of her birthday party, and now here he was, in the hard, solid flesh, standing beside her.

'Jet lagged?'

'A little,' she conceded, grabbing at that as an excuse for her slight breathlessness.

'We'll go straight to the apartment, then,' he suggested. 'We can have dinner there tonight, and take it easy. Tomorrow will be soon enough for you to start seeing the sights.'

She hesitated, slanting him a swift glance from beneath her lashes. 'It's...very kind of you to meet me, but...I'm sure you're very busy,' she murmured a little diffidently. 'You don't have to waste your time going everywhere with me.'

The glint in those dark eyes was unreadable. 'My

pleasure,' he responded. 'Besides, I promised my father I'd take care of you.'

She had been afraid of that. 'Well... Thank you very much,' she murmured wryly.

The drive over Queensboro Bridge to Manhattan made Ginny's head spin, even cocooned in the luxury of Oliver's elegant champagne-coloured Rolls Royce. It was strange to see somewhere so familiar from television and the movies in real life—but nothing on the screen had prepared her for the sheer impact of the place: the cars, the noise, the smell of diesel fumes and every variety of cooking she could imagine, all magnified by the steep cliff walls of glass and concrete that soared above them, seeming to touch the hot blue sky.

But as they turned the corner by Central Park she gasped in delight—quite forgetting her plan to impress him with her air of cool sophistication. The trees were in full bloom, shading the rolling green swathe beneath from the hot afternoon sunshine—a tranquil corner of paradise amid the tall office towers and apartment blocks that hemmed it in on all sides.

The car drew to a halt at the kerb opposite a pair of wide glass doors, beneath a smart dark green awning. Two neatly clipped bay trees in square wooden tubs flanked the doors, which were guarded by a stately doorman whose dark green uniform would have flattered a five-star general.

He stepped forward, opening the car door with a smart salute. 'Good afternoon, Mr. Marsden—good afternoon, miss,' he greeted them, formally polite. 'Traffic's a bit thick this afternoon?'

'It certainly is,' Oliver agreed genially. 'Have Miss Hamilton's bags sent up, will you?'

'Of course, sir.'

Glancing up, Ginny had an impression of a lofty art-deco building, and then the doors slid silently open and she stepped through into a cool marble-paved entrance hall, dappled with sunshine that shone down through the glass atrium roof high above. A charming indoor fountain sparkled amid a bed of indoor palms—a perfect romantic rendezvous for Deborah Kerr and Cary Grant.

'Ohhh…!'

Oliver slanted her an enquiring smile. 'What's up?'

'This!' She stood still, gazing around with bemused wonder. 'It's fabulous!'

He laughed, glancing around as if seeing it himself with new eyes. 'Yes, I suppose it is,' he concurred, pressing the button to summon the old-fashioned wrought-iron lift. 'It was designed by Baughan, who worked with the chap that built the Chrysler building, apparently.'

'Oh?' Ginny was afraid she was supposed to have heard of the Chrysler building—apparently her American education had been sadly lacking.

The lift rose sedately to the top floor, and they stepped out onto an elegant parquet-floored landing. There were two pairs of double doors, one on each side, and as Ginny was still taking in the fact that Oliver's apartment must occupy half of the top floor of the building one of the doors was opened.

'Ah—Ginny, dear. You made it. Do come in.'

Ginny blinked in surprise. 'Alina?'

She gazed at the older woman a little uncertainly—it was nearly ten years since she'd seen Oliver's stepsister, who had married an American businessman she had met in London, and moved to live in Texas. It had come as something as a surprise to everyone at the time, she recalled—they had all believed that she and Oliver would be an 'item'.

Suddenly she felt dowdy and awkward—Alina looked

as if she had stepped straight out of the pages of a glossy magazine. Her willowy figure was set off to perfection by a slimly tailored blue silk suit, her pale gold hair was drawn back into an elegant French pleat, her scarlet lipstick was flawless.

'Of course!' She smiled, gently indulgent. 'But you look exhausted, dear. I'll show you to your room—I'm sure you'll want to freshen up before dinner.'

'Thank you.'

Ginny followed her into the apartment. For some reason she felt a curious sense of deflation; it must just be the effects of jet lag, she reminded herself dismally. She really hadn't expected that she would have Oliver to herself.

After the hustle of the New York streets, the apartment was a haven of tranquillity. A half-flight of steps led down to the main room: tall and spacious, with gleaming wooden floors covered with Chinese rugs, its huge windows were hung with cool white muslin and looked out over the green oasis of Central Park. It was sparely furnished, with four enormous Chesterfields, upholstered in rich dark leather, arranged in a conversational square around a low marble table, lit by a pair of sculptural art-deco standard lamps. To one side was a dining area, raised two steps above the level of the main floor.

On the walls were several large paintings—'daubs' her father would have called them: wild splashes of colour, filled with movement, like whirling dancers or birds in flight. Ginny stared at them, fascinated. Oliver, following her into the room, glanced down at her, a smile in his eyes.

'Do you like them?' he asked quietly.

She hesitated, her head tipped slightly on one side as she studied the largest of the canvases—a firestorm of red and orange, shot through with vivid green. 'I'm not quite sure,' she confessed. 'It's...certainly unusual...'

Alina laughed lightly. 'Now, Oliver, you can't expect the poor child to start giving you opinions on modern art when she's only just arrived! But we'll take her to the Met, and the Museum of Modern Art—would you like that, Ginny?'

Ginny forced some kind of smile; she had been looking forward to this trip so much, but she wasn't sure that she was going to enjoy it if Alina was going to be there all the time, treating her like an infant being given an ice-cream cone. But she really mustn't be ungrateful, she chided herself firmly—Alina was just trying to be friendly.

Alina had crossed the room to open a door on the far side, which led into a wide passage, off which there were more rooms. Ginny caught a fleeting glimpse of a white-tiled kitchen, and what appeared to be a study, and then Alina threw open another door.

'Here you are—this is your room,' she announced. 'The bathroom is through there. We'll be having dinner in about an hour—will that be okay for you?'

Ginny blinked. 'Oh...yes... Whatever's c-convenient,' she stammered, gazing around, a little overwhelmed. A film-star would have felt at home in this room. It was about three times the size of her bedroom at home, with a side-view of the park. The carpet was cream, and long drapes of cream-coloured muslin hung at the windows.

The wide bed was covered with a cream throw of quilted satin—it seemed almost sacrilegious to sit down on it. But she was so tired...and she had time for just a few minutes' rest before she started getting ready for dinner. Carefully turning back the quilt, she kicked off her shoes and lay down, watching the muslin drapes as they stirred gently in the warm flow of air from the air-conditioning grilles in the ceiling above them.

She really shouldn't have been surprised to see Alina here with Oliver, she reminded herself—after all, she was his stepsister. Besides, in spite of her glamorous appearance, she really hadn't had a very happy life. Her first marriage—to a wealthy older man—had ended in divorce by the time she was twenty-one, and her second, too, was apparently heading in the same direction, according to Aunt Margot.

It was really rather silly to let herself be jealous of her—it must be sad to have been married twice and to have had neither of them work out. And it was nice for her to have her stepbrother to turn to, when her mother was so far away. There was no reason to suppose there was anything more to it than that.

Yawning, she glanced at her watch. She really ought to get up and start getting dressed for dinner. Just another couple of minutes...

When next she opened her eyes, the room was full of morning sunshine.

Startled, she sat up—realising with a shock of surprise that she was beneath the covers and in her nightdress. Her clothes were neatly folded over one of the square leather armchairs by the window—and she was almost certain she hadn't put them there herself. Alina must have helped her.

Scrambling out of bed, she found that her suitcases had been unpacked and everything put neatly away in the walk-in closet next to the bathroom. She frowned slightly—she couldn't imagine Alina doing that. But then she couldn't imagine Oliver doing it either. And what would the sophisticated Alina have made of Mr. Honey, the battered old teddy bear that had been tucked

into a corner of one of her cases, and was now propped
up perkily on the other leather armchair?

By the time she had had a shower in the elegant
thirties-style bathroom, and changed into one of the out-
fits she had bought especially for this trip—a long-line
jersey-knit jacket in a warm shade of coral-pink, teamed
with a simple charcoal-grey top and softly tailored trousers—she thought she might be ready to face the pair of
them.

But when she walked into the sitting room she found
Oliver alone at a table on the wide balcony overlooking
the park, reading the paper as he finished his breakfast.
He was casually dressed today, in a white linen shirt and
cream-coloured chinos, and he glanced up, greeting her
with a genial smile as he folded his paper. 'Well, good
morning, sleepy-head. Feeling better?'

'Yes, thank you,' she responded, fighting the sudden
tightness in her throat. 'I'm...sorry I missed dinner.'

'Ah, there, honey, you were so tired you didn't even
wake when I put you to bed.' Another voice, warmed
by a hint of Caribbean sunshine, came from behind her.
'You were sleeping tighter than a cricket in a rug.'

'Oh...' Ginny responded, blinking in some surprise at
the motherly woman who had bustled out from the
kitchen with a glass jug that wafted a delicious aroma
of freshly filtered coffee. 'It was you who...put me to
bed, then?' she queried, somewhat relieved that the mys-
tery had been so prosaically solved.

'Sure it was, honey,' the housekeeper chuckled, her
black eyes twinkling. 'Who else would it have been?'

'Ginny, this is Willa,' Oliver explained with a slightly
crooked smile. 'She's the boss around here.'

'That's right!' the amiable woman agreed with a rich
chuckle. 'I never did know a man who could take proper
care of hisself. Reading stock prices at the breakfast ta-

ble…!' She snatched the paper away—clearly this was an argument frequently re-run. 'How d'you expect to start the day right 'less you pay attention to your stomach first?'

'If you pay any more attention to your stomach, we'll need to have the doors widened!' he retaliated swiftly.

'Huh!' The good lady half turned, wiggling her wide rear with pride. 'I'm a whole lotta woman, I ain't denying! Now, honey, what'll you have for breakfast?' she added to Ginny. 'Muffins? Toast and eggs?'

'I'd like to try some muffins, please,' Ginny responded, mindful that Willa was unlikely to approve of her skimping on her breakfast for the sake of her figure—and in truth far too hungry to even consider it.

The housekeeper's wide face beamed with approval. 'That's a good girl. You sit down and have some coffee, and your muffins will be right up.'

'Thank you…' Ginny murmured, taking a seat at the other place that had been set at the table.

Oliver picked up the coffee jug, pouring for both of them. 'So, what would you like to do today?' he asked.

'Don't you have to go to work?' she queried a little shyly.

'It's Saturday,' he reminded her, his dark eyes smiling.

'Oh… Of course…' She felt a faint blush of pink colour her cheeks. 'Well… What do you suggest?'

'We could start with the World Trade Center—that's the place for the best views. And I expect you'll want to see the Statue of Liberty?'

'Oh, yes,' she agreed eagerly. 'And according to the book I read I have to take a trip on the Staten Island Ferry.'

Oliver nodded. 'Okay. We'll make a start as soon as

you've finished your breakfast, then—we're going to have a busy day.'

'Will...Alina be coming?' she queried, struggling to keep her voice neutral as she stirred her coffee.

'Alina?' He looked faintly surprised. 'No, of course not. Oh, Willa, could you bring me some more toast?' he added as the housekeeper returned with Ginny's muffins.

CHAPTER THREE

THE next few days were a whirl of excitement. They took a buggy ride through Central Park, they wandered around Chinatown, they argued cheerfully over the architectural merits of the Guggenheim Museum, and every night they ate from a different region of the world. Ginny could honestly say that she had never enjoyed herself so much in her life.

She had never dreamed that Oliver could be so much fun to be with. At first she had been still a little shy of him, afraid he would think her immature or silly, but she had soon begun to relax as she found that he had a dry sense of humour, and that they laughed at the same things. It had been a surprise, too, that he was so willing to spend his time traipsing around the shops and tourist sights, never seeming to be bored.

And there was no sign of Alina; Ginny didn't want to ask again where she was, and Oliver didn't mention her.

Nor did she want to ask why he wasn't at work. But then on the Thursday morning she arrived at breakfast to find him talking on the telephone. She hesitated, but he motioned to her to sit down, so she poured herself some coffee and spread a generous swathe of butter and honey on one of Willa's delicious fresh-baked muffins. A starling had hopped onto the balcony rail, its head tipped hopefully to one side, so she dropped a few crumbs on the floor for it, watching with delight as it hopped to within inches of her feet.

Oliver took several calls, and then at last put the

phone down. 'Sorry about that,' he apologised with a wry grimace. 'Business.'

'Oh... Yes, of course.' She hesitated, stirring her coffee. 'Will you...have to go to your office today?' she enquired tentatively.

He shook his head, lazily tipping back his wicker chair until it rested against the rail of the balcony and stretching his arms above his head. 'I've taken the week off,' he declared. 'I work hard—I deserved it.'

'Oh...' From beneath her lashes, she smiled at him a little shyly. 'You...didn't have to waste it all showing me around,' she murmured.

'It hasn't been wasted.'

Her heart did a kind of somersault. The way he was looking at her, the way he was smiling... No—she was just imagining it. She *had* to keep her fantasies under control, or he would guess, and then she would feel like a complete idiot. 'What is it you do, exactly?' she enquired, trying to make conversation.

'It's called "arbitrage". Basically I buy and sell futures, and make money out of the differential rates between two markets. Say it's copper—once upon a time people would simply trade in copper shares. Then people began to speculate that the price would move in a certain direction—up or down. So they'd agree to buy the shares at a certain price, on a certain day in the future—or sometimes to sell shares they hadn't yet bought. The point is, they'd only have to put up a small percentage of the money.'

'So if the price of the shares moved in the direction they'd predicted, they could pocket the profits without having had to spend very much of their own money in the first place?' she queried, fascinated.

'That's right. Anyway, pretty soon people began buying and selling the options as if they were shares, and the whole thing took off. By 1983 the dollar value of the futures trade exceeded the dollar value of trading on the whole New York Stock Exchange.'

'It sounds a bit like gambling.'

'It is. Of course, you have to know your markets pretty thoroughly, but you're walking a tightrope—there's always a chance you could fall flat on your face.'

'It sounds exciting!' she remarked, her eyes shining.

'Want to come and see?'

'We can visit the Stock Exchange?'

He nodded. 'Finish your breakfast, and I'll call Devlin to bring the car around.'

It was amusing to visit the Stock Exchange with someone who actually worked there. He took her to the public viewing gallery, from where she could look down through the glass onto the crowded floor, with its famous octagonal trading posts mounted with monitors screening all the latest prices, its brokers and reporters in their colourful blazers.

'It looks like chaos!' she remarked, watching a minor stampede to one corner as some new price was announced. 'How on earth do they all know what's going on?'

'Herd instinct,' Oliver responded dryly. 'It's nothing like what it used to be, though—most of the trading is done by computers now.'

'Anyway, I wouldn't want to be the person who has to sweep up at the end of the day,' she remarked, casting a wry glance at the swathes of litter piling up on the floor.

He laughed, and with a gesture of which he didn't seem aware let his hand rest on the small of her back as he led her on, first to see the exhibition of the exchange's history, and then into the part that was barred from the public, where he casually introduced her to several of his colleagues and laughingly waved aside any attempt to talk business.

'Not this week—I'm just a tourist!' he insisted. 'We're off down to Battery Park, to eat ice-creams and watch the ferry.'

The streets of lower Manhattan were baking in the late morning sun, but on the green promontory at its southern tip a gentle breeze was blowing in across the bay. As promised, Oliver bought ice-creams—huge double cornets, with nuts and chocolate sauce—from one of the stalls around the fringes of the park, and they sat on the grass while he pointed out to her the various landmarks they could see.

Ginny slanted Oliver a smiling glance, her eyes dancing. 'You've got ice-cream on your chin,' she giggled.

'I do?' He took a handkerchief from his pocket and dabbed. 'Better?'

'No—it's there.' Without thinking, she reached out to brush it away with her thumb—but just as she was about to touch him she hesitated, her hand trembling. It almost seemed as though there was an electrical charge between them... But he was looking at her, a glint of quizzical amusement in those deep, dark eyes, and she knew that she was giving herself away. He knew.

His skin was warm, just slightly roughened along the hard line of his jaw. She smeared away the smudge of ice-cream, withdrawing her hand quickly, her eyes looking anywhere but into his. There was a long moment of silence; all she seemed able to hear was the sound of her own breathing, the racing beat of her heart...

Suddenly an odd movement a dozen yards away caught her eye. An elderly man was staggering, and as she watched in horror he slowly toppled to the ground beside the path. She scrambled to her feet, shocked to see that people were just walking past, ignoring him. 'He's ill!' she gasped, hurrying forward.

Oliver was beside her. 'He's probably just drunk,' he warned.

'No.' She knelt beside him, taking his hand, worried by how clammy it felt. How did you check a pulse? 'Get on your mobile and call for an ambulance,' she commanded Oliver urgently, all her awe of him forgotten.

She really didn't know why she was so sure the old man wasn't drunk—maybe it was just contrariness, because everyone else seemed to be assuming that he was. But he didn't look like a drunk—he had a kindly face. He could have been someone's grandfather.

Two men in sharp business suits had paused, staring down with an expression of disdain. 'Damned winos,' one of them remarked scornfully, and they walked on.

Oliver frowned, and pulled his mobile from his pocket. He spoke into it swiftly, and then knelt beside her, touching the old man's forehead with his hand and then bending over him to smell his breath. 'Pear drops!' he diagnosed grimly. 'You were right—he's no wino. He's in a diabetic coma.' Deftly he loosened the man's tie and shirt collar to make him more comfortable.

'He's wearing one of those SOS things round his neck,' Ginny pointed out. 'It'll have his name and address in it.'

'And his insurance details,' Oliver added dryly. 'Unless he's on Medicare.'

Ginny frowned. 'Is that a problem?'

'The ambulance people will want to know—so they'll know which hospital to take him to. And who's going to pay their bill.'

'Well, I will, of course,' she insisted, without even thinking about it. 'I wonder if he has a wife? She'll be worried sick about him. Ah, is that the ambulance?' she added, lifting her head to listen for the sound of a siren.

It was late by the time they left the hospital—the old man, it transpired, was a widower, and his only daughter lived in Philadelphia, so Ginny had insisted on staying until she arrived. Oliver, a little to her surprise, stayed with her—nor did he complain once. As they climbed into the back of his Rolls Royce, which had come to collect them, he slanted her a slightly crooked smile.

'Had you forgotten that we were going to the Richmond tonight?' he asked.

'Oh... Yes, I had,' she confessed wryly. 'I'm sorry. Are we too late now?'

'That depends how long it will take you to get ready,' he responded, a quirk of amusement in his voice.

'Not long—I promise.'

He laughed teasingly. 'How often have I heard a woman say that?'

It was a throwaway line, but it caught at Ginny's heart—she would have preferred not to have to think about the women he went out with. She knew perfectly well that although he seemed to have enjoyed this past week with her it had been no more than an interlude for him, a novelty. Oliver Marsden, licking ice-cream cones in Battery Park? No way.

But at least tonight she could try to impress him—both by being as quick as she had promised and by looking her very best. And she couldn't quite suppress a little quiver of excitement as she got ready. She had brought the dress with her in the wild hope that she might get a chance to wear it, and as soon as Oliver had suggested dining at the Richmond she had decided that it would be perfect.

A sheath of matt black satin, very simple and elegant,

it had a strapless top cut low across the line of her breasts, leaving her shoulders bare, and a long slim skirt that skimmed her slender curves all the way down to her smart black evening sandals. She was getting quite adept at putting her hair up—though it obstinately refused to curl, it was easy enough to coil into a neat twist on the crown of her head—and her only jewellery was a simple gold chain with matching earrings in the shape of leaves.

When she had finished, she stood back to subject her reflection to a critical assessment. Yes, she had been right to keep her make-up light—it had been tempting to go for scarlet lipstick, but instinct had warned her that it would be a touch too much. Even without it she looked quite sufficiently grown-up, and...yes, sophisticated.

A small smile of anticipation curved her soft mouth as she picked up her handbag. What would Oliver say when he saw her? Would he like it...? Drawing in a long, deep breath to steady her jangling nerves, she opened the door, and with a conscious grace walked along the passage to the sitting room.

But when she got there, she found that Oliver was on the phone. She hesitated, ready to retreat, not wanting to eavesdrop, but he held up his hand. 'Okay, Alina—I'll be right over. No, it doesn't matter. Ten minutes, okay?'

Disappointment so sharp it felt like a knife stabbed at her heart. But as he put the phone down and turned to her she forced a bright smile into place. 'Is there something wrong?' she asked.

He looked at her, but she felt as if he wasn't seeing her—he didn't seem to even notice the dress. 'I'm afraid so. I'm sorry, Ginny—we won't be able to make it to the Richmond tonight, after all. Something...urgent has come up.'

'Oh...that's all right.' She had never been more grateful for the long years of practice that enabled her to keep the smile firmly glued in place. 'We've been gadding around so much, I could do with a night in for a change.'

He nodded absently, choosing to believe her. 'Tomorrow we'll go down to South Street, and have lunch in one of the restaurants where they cook the fish straight off the wharf,' he promised, shrugging into his dinner jacket, already halfway out of the door. 'Goodnight.'

The door closed behind him and Ginny stood alone in the middle of the vast room, all dressed up with nowhere to go, the lights of Manhattan twinkling through the window to her left as the tears trickled slowly down her cheeks.

Whatever it was that had made Oliver dash off so urgently to Alina's side kept him away all night—Ginny was quite sure of that, because his bedroom was opposite hers, and she would have heard him come in. And she hadn't slept a wink. She had lain awake all night, telling herself not to be so stupid.

After all, he had spent all week with her. It was unreasonable to expect him to dance around her the whole time. And Alina was his stepsister—she had a greater right to his attention than the mere daughter of an old family friend.

And what if Alina was more than just his stepsister? She had known all along he was out of her league anyway—he was just being kind to her because he was...well, that kind of person. Surely she had never let herself be deluded even for a *second* into believing he might actually find her attractive in the...man-woman sense?

She couldn't even begin to compare herself with Alina. It wasn't just that she was beautiful, with a cool, aristocratic perfection that was usually only seen on the pages of *Vogue,* but she dressed with an understated style—and had the perfect figure to show off her clothes. It was that air of poise, of *savoir-faire,* of sophisticated self-assurance which Ginny could only envy.

Nor was it something that she herself could hope to acquire with maturity—it was something Alina had always had. She had been sixteen when her mother had married Oliver's father—a year older than Oliver—but even at that age she had shown no sign of awkward adolescence. The two girls had been bridesmaids at the wedding, and to the six-year-old Ginny she had seemed like some kind of princess.

The sun rose early—by five-thirty it was already slanting its way in through the muslin curtains as the sky lightened to a clear summer blue. Ginny clambered wearily out of bed—she ached from lying there all night trying to make herself fall asleep. She might as well get herself some orange juice—and if Oliver came back and wondered what she was doing up so early, well…she could always think up some excuse.

But though she sat out on the balcony in her dressing gown, sipping her orange juice as the sun rose higher above the man-made stalagmites on the eastern side of the park and the traffic below built up to its daytime cacophony, Oliver didn't return. It was Willa's day off, so she made herself some breakfast, though she couldn't eat more than a few crumbs.

At about eleven o'clock she decided that it would appear rather more cool and self-contained if she wasn't found sitting here waiting for him to come home—and besides, she wanted to buy a present for her father. So she got dressed and boldly ventured out to the shops on Columbus Avenue, where she managed to waste at least a couple of hours dawdling around the fashionable boutiques and galleries.

But it was really rather too hot to be out—'The sort

of day you have to change your shirt three times between the car and the porch,' as she had heard Oliver describe it. So with some reluctance she made her way back to the apartment. There was a different doorman on duty from the one who had been there all week—she had started to make friends with the other one, exchanging a few words with him every time they went in and out, but she didn't know this one apart from nodding to him as she had left this morning.

It was a little weird, being in a strange city where she didn't know a soul, where she hadn't spoken a word to anyone all morning except, 'I'll have this one,' and, 'Thank you,' to the assistant in the shop where she had bought a silver bookmark for her father, engraved with a crest of an American Eagle. It was probably the first time in her entire life that she had gone for so long without having someone to talk to.

Oliver was still not home; it was strange how you could sense that a place was empty as soon as you opened the door. With a kind of half-hearted optimism she looked around to see if there was a note—perhaps he had been in and gone out again. But there was nothing. She had a bowl of cornflakes for lunch, and then plopped herself down in front of the television, flicking aimlessly through the channels.

It was almost six o'clock when she heard the click of the lock in the door behind her. Quickly schooling her features into an expression of cool composure, she glanced up over her shoulder as he came in.

'Oh…hi,' she greeted him with casual unconcern.

'Hi.' He looked drained. He was still wearing the evening shirt he had been wearing last night, but it was no longer pressed and pristine. He had taken off his tie, leaving the collar loosely open, and his beautifully cut jacket was slung casually across his shoulder. But he managed some kind of crooked smile. 'Sorry I've been so long.'

'Oh, that's okay,' she responded lightly. 'I was just watching television.'

He glanced at the screen, one dark eyebrow arching in quizzical enquiry. 'You're learning Spanish?'

'Oh...' Damn—she hadn't even realised that she was watching a Hispanic channel. 'No, I...the film I was watching just finished, and I was flicking over to see what was on. Isn't that the one that was in *Mandate?* See—the tall one, just going out of the door.'

He laughed, shrugging his wide shoulders. 'I wouldn't have a clue. So, is that what you've been doing today— watching television?'

'Oh, no.' She was glad now that she could truthfully say she hadn't. 'I went shopping. Not far—just round to Columbus. It was fun. I bought a present for Pops.'

He nodded, though she sensed that his interest was no more than polite. He had hooked his jacket over the stair-newel, and after crossing the room he folded himself lazily into one of the other Chesterfields, his long legs stretched out in front of him, his arms folded behind his head. For a moment he closed his eyes.

Ginny watched him, her heart aching. If he had looked happy, she would have been grateful to Alina, in spite of the bitter jealousy that was tearing at her insides. She would simply have been glad to see him content. But he looked exhausted. What had happened? What sort of fatal allure did that woman have that she could make a man like that drop everything and rush to her side at a moment's notice, and then send him home looking as if he had been through a wringer?

She would never do that to him. She only wanted to love him, to kiss away the frown from around his eyes, to warm his weary body with hers. If only he would let her, she would give him everything...

As he opened his eyes she swiftly put those wild, wanton thoughts to the back of her mind, returning him only a smile.

'So, any thoughts about where you'd like to eat tonight?' he asked. 'We can try the Richmond again, if you like—you usually have to book ahead, but I dare say we could wangle a table.'

'Oh, I don't know...' She shrugged in casual unconcern. 'Actually, I'm not sure if I really want to eat out tonight—I have to pack, and be away fairly early in the morning. Couldn't we have dinner here for a change?'

She was rewarded by the flicker of relief that passed behind his eyes. 'You're sure? We could send out for something...'

'Oh, no. Why don't you let me cook something? That is, if Willa wouldn't mind me messing around in her kitchen. It could be my thank-you to you for showing me round.'

His smile was all the compensation she needed for her misery since yesterday evening. 'All right. Thank you— that sounds like a very nice idea. And Ginny...' he added as she jumped up and started for the kitchen.

She turned, a question in her eyes.

'Wear that black dress you put on last night,' he said, an odd note in his voice that she couldn't quite fathom. 'I liked that.'

She nodded, suddenly not trusting her voice to speak. He *had* noticed the dress...

Fortunately Willa kept her cupboards well stocked, so there were plenty of options. She chose a fairly easy menu—gammon steaks with honey and ginger, which she could serve with stir-fry vegetables. The starter was a clever fraud that she could knock together while the steaks were under the grill—a tin of sweetcorn stirred into some chicken stock, with a generous lashing of cream. *Presto!*—a delicious soup. And for dessert they could have a coconut custard, decorated with flaked almonds and slices of kiwi fruit.

In between preparing the dishes she managed to have a quick shower. The dress was back on its hanger, and she got it out and hung it on the back of the wardrobe door. Was it really only twenty-four hours ago that she had put it on, her heart full of such foolish dreams? That had been before the phone call from Alina. How much older and wiser she felt now, than that silly young girl.

Although...he *had* noticed the dress...

She decided not to put her hair up tonight—as they weren't going out, it seemed a little over the top. Instead she brushed it until it was gleaming, and left it hanging loose and straight down her back—it reached almost to her waist now. A quick slick of pink lipstick, a smudge of shadow around her eyes and a touch of mascara to emphasise her long lashes, and she was ready.

When she returned to the sitting room, she found that although Oliver had changed into casual clothes he had laid the dining table, setting it with candles, and was opening a bottle of wine. He glanced up as she walked into the room, his dark eyes sliding down over her as she stood hesitantly in the doorway, struggling to control her ragged breathing, the racing beat of her heart. But he said nothing—he merely nodded in what she hoped was approval.

The aroma from the kitchen told her that dinner was almost ready. 'I'll...bring in the soup,' she managed, hoping he wouldn't notice the slight tremor in her voice.

Not even the Richmond could have been more romantic. As the sun had set a blue dusk had gathered over the tops of the trees in Central Park, darkening slowly as if a velvet cloak was sweeping in across the sky. The glow of the candles reflected in the long window—five points of warm golden light against the bright lights of Fifth Avenue across the park, and beyond them again, high and distant, far out of reach, the cold sequin spangle of the stars. They ate in silence. Maybe tomorrow there would be a strike by the air-traffic controllers at Kennedy Airport, and she would have to stay longer...

The meal ended, Oliver insisted that she stay where she was while he took the plates to the kitchen and stacked them in the dishwasher. He returned with coffee. She watched as he stirred a small amount of cream into his, wondering what he was thinking. Was it about Alina?

'That was an excellent meal,' he remarked, his eyes smiling at her across the table in the way that always made her heartbeat accelerate. 'I don't think we could have done better at the Richmond.'

She returned the smile, glad of the soft light of the candles to conceal the blush of pink in her cheeks. 'Thank you,' she murmured.

He leaned back lazily in his chair, sipping his coffee. 'So, have you enjoyed New York?' he enquired.

'Yes, I have—very much. Thank you for...spending so much time with me.' She stirred her own coffee, the silver spoon tinkling against the elegant dark green china, her eyes focused in abstract concentration on the swirl of cream as it slowly melted away. 'I'm...afraid it was your father who corralled you into it,' she murmured, slanting him a shy glance from beneath her lashes.

He laughed dryly. 'Well, yes,' he acknowledged, that fascinating mouth twisting in sardonic humour, 'It was his idea—he and your father dreamed it up between them. And I think we can assume that a week in New York isn't the limit of their ambition.'

Her heart gave a sharp thud, and she stared at him, startled.

There was an enigmatic amusement in those dark eyes. 'I rather suspect they're hoping to see us married.'

The blush of pink in her cheeks deepened to a hot scarlet. 'What a...silly idea,' she protested, struggling for breath.

'Do you really think so?' He reached across the table and took her hand in his, stroking one fingertip lightly across her palm as her breath caught in the back of her throat. 'Sweet, virginal Virginia... Actually, I think it's rather a good idea.'

CHAPTER FOUR

'HIDING, Ginny? That's not like you.'

Oliver's sardonic query made Ginny turn sharply, her brittle smile swiftly concealing the pain of those haunting old memories. 'Just taking a little breather,' she responded lightly. 'It's so desperately hot in there. Besides, you can't expect me to dance till dawn without at least a couple of minutes' break.'

'I suppose not,' he conceded on a note of dry amusement. 'You've been the life of the party tonight—as usual. You seem to have danced with almost everyone—except me. I thought you might like to remedy that omission?'

Her heart kicked sharply against her ribs, but she managed to make herself laugh merrily. 'Well, since you've paid such a high price for me, I can scarcely refuse, can I?' she retorted, daring a hint of mockery.

A glint of something she couldn't quite read flickered in the depths of those dark eyes. 'I've paid for considerably more than one dance,' he reminded her, letting his gaze drift down to linger over the firm, creamy ripeness of her breasts, so invitingly packaged by the low, sweeping neckline and tight whale-boned bodice of her dress. He was deliberately seeking to unsettle her, she was quite sure, but she could do nothing to suppress the hot blush of pink that rose to her cheeks.

She tilted up her chin, determined not to let him see that he could have any effect on her; she had made that mistake once before, when she had been too young to defend herself against his ruthless charm. She had learned a lot since then. Hiding her reluctance behind a gracious smile, she accepted the imperious hand he held out to her—but as she moved towards the ballroom he drew her back.

'You're right—it's hot in there. We can hear the music just as well out here.'

She stiffened in automatic resistance as he drew her into his arms. It wasn't that she hadn't danced with him since the disastrous ending of their engagement—once or twice when he had been in England they had found themselves at the same party, and it would have been quite ridiculous to ignore each other, given their family connections. Besides, they had apparently both been equally anxious to deflect the curiosity of the gossips by behaving as if they had never been anything more than friendly acquaintances.

But somehow tonight it was different. For reasons of his own Oliver had chosen to stir things up with that outrageous bid. And now, for reasons of his own, he was insisting on dancing out here on the terrace, just the two of them, alone in the moonlight, as the sweet scent of jasmine drifted around them on the night air...

Quickly she dismissed such treacherously romantic thoughts from her mind and fixed her best coquettish smile in place, tilting back her head to look up at him. 'So, what exactly is it you want me to do for all that money?' she enquired, her voice carrying an inflection of defiant humour.

He laughed, low and husky, taunting her with every outrageous possibility her foolish mind had conjured since the moment Cornell Elliot had clacked down his gavel. 'Something that requires your...unique talents,' he responded, again letting his gaze linger over the warm, ripe curves of her breasts, seeming fascinated by the way every ragged breath she took crushed them more tightly against the soft green velvet.

A hot rush of fever flooded her veins, and she had to struggle to hold onto even a semblance of her poise. Arching one finely drawn eyebrow in cool enquiry, she forced herself to meet his mocking dark eyes. 'Oh...?'

He smiled, switching abruptly to a pose of bland innocence that reminded her—if she'd ever needed reminding—just how deceptive he could be. 'I want you to arrange a party.'

She let go of her breath very carefully, so that it wouldn't sound as if she was sighing with relief. 'Something special, I take it?'

'Howard's retirement. We're having a family party, of course, for his seventieth birthday, but I want to have one at the bank as well. It will be an opportunity to invite some of his business associates from the past fifty years.'

'Of course,' she agreed, a little surprised. 'I'd be delighted to do it.'

He laughed dryly. 'That's rather fortunate, since you don't have an option. Unless you want me to ask for my thousand pounds back from the organising committee?'

She conceded a smile, shaking her head. 'Don't be silly,' she responded. 'Have you drawn up a guest list?'

'I think I have most of the names, but I'd like you to come into the office and see his secretary some time— she'll be able to remember any I've overlooked, as well as advise you on anything else you need to know.'

She nodded. 'Fine. What date do you have in mind?'

'Sometime next month? Will that be enough time to organise everything?'

'I should think so. Of course, it will depend on the caterers—they tend to get quite booked up. But I know one or two good ones who may be able to fit us in.'

'Excellent,' he approved, an inflection of that familiar

sardonic mockery in his voice. 'I shall leave it all in your hands, then.'

She kept her smile in place, while from beneath her lashes she studied him with a covert suspicion. They were both playing a game, pretending that there was no more to this than a simple arrangement between friends—and if it hadn't been for their shared history that was exactly what it would be. But given that history...somehow it didn't quite add up.

'What I don't quite understand,' she purred, all sweetness, 'is why you should pay out all that money to have me do it? Why don't you simply ask Alina?'

He laughed, only a flickering glint somewhere deep in his eyes hinting at the dark undercurrents beneath their charade. 'Anyone would think you were trying to wriggle out of it,' he taunted softly.

'Of course not!' she protested. 'I made a promise.'

'So you did,' he murmured, a hard edge in his voice. 'And this time I intend to see that you keep it.'

An icy chill snatched at her heart; he wasn't just talking about the party. She had been right— he had neither forgotten nor forgiven. She tried to draw back, but his arms had tightened almost imperceptibly around her, curving her closer against him, making it clear that he had no intention of letting her escape until he was ready to set her free.

Perhaps she really couldn't blame him; after all, he only knew half of the story—the half everyone else knew. She was quite sure Alina would never have told him the truth. But she had spent the past six years trying to convince herself that there was no point crying over what couldn't be changed, that it had probably all been for the best anyway—until she had almost come to believe that the scars had healed.

And now the cloak she had drawn across the past had

started to come unravelled, and it hurt to look back at her nineteen-year-old self—so innocent, so besotted, scarcely able to believe that the object of her adolescent crush had even deigned to look her way, let alone ask her to marry him. He could have had any woman he wanted—but he had fallen in love with her!

It was that vulnerability that Alina had played on—that and her own stupid, stubborn pride...

The engagement party had been her father's idea—in collusion with his partner in crime once again. It seemed as though the whole world had been invited. Ginny had been a little apprehensive about it at first, but now, dancing with Oliver, she felt as if her heart was flying. Was it really possible to be so happy? Surely it was tempting fate?

For about the millionth time she slanted a surreptitious glance at the ring on the third finger of her left hand. It was so beautiful—a clear, pure emerald, square-cut, surrounded by fourteen diamonds. She was still not quite used to the weight of it—and she doubted that she would ever tire of turning it to the light so that the fire in its green heart sparkled into life.

Oliver smiled down at her, a glint of amusement in his dark eyes. 'Admiring your ring again?' he teased gently.

'Of course.' She returned his smile, joy bubbling inside her like the fizz of champagne. 'It's the most beautiful engagement ring in the whole history of the world!'

He laughed, that low, mellow sound that she loved so much. 'I'm glad you like it.'

She was dancing on a cloud. Apart from the night of her birthday party, this was the first time she had danced with Oliver—in fact, it was almost the first time she had really been in his arms. For most of the past six weeks she had only been able to talk to him on the telephone. He had rung her every night, but it wasn't the same as being with him. And she had chewed herself up with worrying that when he saw her again he would have second thoughts about that unexpected proposal.

But now at last he was here, and everything was going to be all right. Wasn't it...?

Her eyes came to rest on a willowy blonde across the room, in a pencil-slim black dress. She was talking to one of Oliver's friends, her slender hands making some graceful gesture to emphasise a point. Something she had said had clearly amused him—he was laughing, totally absorbed in her, his expression betraying that he could scarcely believe his luck that this stunning creature was paying attention to him.

Something uncomfortable knotted in Ginny's stomach. It had been a surprise when she had found out that Alina had returned to England with Oliver—he hadn't mentioned it when he had called. She had tried to tell herself that it was of no significance—after all, it was only natural that she would want to come home now that her second marriage was over.

And she had tried to hide her disappointment when she had joined them for what Ginny had been looking forward to as their first romantic dinner-date together. In truth, she hadn't quite known what to say—even when the following day he had cancelled their plans because he was taking Alina to visit some friends. She didn't want him to think she was going to be clingy or demanding...

'You're very quiet,' Oliver murmured softly, his breath warm against her cheek as he bent his head close to hers. 'What are you thinking about?'

'Oh...I... Nothing, I'm...just a bit tired, that's all.' She was just being silly. She had no reason to be jealous of Alina—after all, it was *her* he had asked to marry him. 'There's been so much to do. And you've been so...tied up—I hardly seem to have seen you since you got back from New York.'

He seemed to draw back from her slightly, lifting his head. 'I'm sorry,' he responded, a splinter of irritation in his voice. 'I've had a lot of demands on my time.'

'I know. I just... I thought maybe we would have a chance to be together a little bit...'

'We've got all of next week,' he reminded her a little sharply. 'We can do whatever you like.'

'I know...' She was beginning to regret that she had even raised the subject—surely they weren't going to have their first quarrel on the very night they got engaged? 'But...then you'll be going back to New York again, and I won't see you for ages.'

'I have to work.' His words were dismissive, though his tone wasn't unkind.

'I know that.' She felt a flicker of resentment; he was treating her like a silly little schoolgirl again. 'It's just that...I want to be with you...'

The eyes she lifted to his face were misted with tears, and he smiled, tilting up her chin with one finger. 'I know. I'm sorry—it's been...difficult. But it won't always be like this. We'll be married in a couple of months, and then we can be together as much as you want.'

He bent his head again, and his mouth brushed over hers lightly, fleetingly. A sudden fierce hunger that she barely understood welled up inside her, and she curved herself against him, her lips parting in desperate invitation. She wanted him to kiss her properly—she *needed* him to kiss her properly. But he couldn't, not here.

When they were married... It was only a couple of months away. She could wait that long... And Oliver loved her—why else would he want to marry her? Perhaps it was just as well if he…held back a little bit. Oh, she had kissed plenty of boys, but she had never been kissed by someone as…experienced as Oliver. She still needed a little time to get used to it.

It seemed as though everyone wanted to hug her, admire her ring, wish her happy—aunts and cousins she only ever saw at weddings and funerals. It was exhausting. But at last she found a chance to slip away for a few minutes to her bedroom, to comb her hair and check that her lipstick was still in place. Satisfied that she still looked presentable, she drew in a few deep, steadying breaths, steeling herself to return to the fray.

But as she stepped out into the shadowy corridor she almost collided with Alina. 'Oh… Hello…' She managed to recover herself, quickly hiding all her heart-burning doubts and uncertainties behind a bright smile. 'Were you looking for the bathroom? It's the other way—second door on the left.'

'Thank you,' Alina responded graciously—somehow her smile never quite seemed to reach her eyes. 'As a matter of fact I was looking for you.'

'Oh…?' Ginny felt an uncomfortable little chill feather over her skin; perhaps there was a cold draught in this corridor.

'I thought we should have a little talk. Is this your room?'

She stepped past Ginny without waiting for an invitation, pushing open the door. Her eyes took in with one glance the pink ruffles and the row of stuffed furry animals lined up attentively along the chaise longue at the end of the bed. She didn't need to say a thing—Ginny could guess exactly what she was thinking.

'So…' She moved over and sat down elegantly on the bed, politely ignoring Mr. Honey, whose favoured place was on the pillows. 'Congratulations, my dear. Let me see the ring?'

Ginny held out her hand.

'Ah, how lovely! I told Oliver it should be an emerald. You didn't want a solitaire, did you?'

'No...' An uncomfortable little ache had begun in the region of her heart; she didn't want to know that Oliver had taken Alina's advice over the choice of her ring.

'And you'll be getting married in three months. A fall wedding—so romantic! You know, I was married for the first time at about the same age as you are. Too young, most people said, but I wouldn't listen.' She shrugged her slim shoulders. 'Of course, Larry was older than me. Ten years. Quite a substantial gap, don't you think?'

Ginny was beginning to feel as if the walls were closing in around her. Alina wasn't merely pointing out an amusing coincidence.

'I was dreadfully disillusioned,' the older woman went on, a wistful note in her voice. 'I should hate to watch you go through the same thing. Men of that age, you know, have grown out of the romantic flights of youth—when they choose to marry, it tends to be for quite specific reasons.'

Ginny's heart was pounding, and she wasn't quite sure if she could trust herself to speak. 'Such as...?'

'Well, in Oliver's case, obviously he needs a son—an heir to carry on the family name. It would be different if he had a brother, of course, but as it is...' Again that elegant little shrug. 'That's why I told him to marry someone else. I can't have children, you see.'

She smiled, a sad, sweet smile, reaching out one slim, manicured hand to straighten the teddy bear, which had fallen askew on the pillows. 'I hope I haven't distressed you,' she purred. 'But I do think it's best that you should understand the way things are, don't you? I'm sure you'll make a perfect little wife for Oliver, so long as you don't make the mistake of believing that he's in love with you.'

And, rising gracefully to her feet, she wafted from the room, leaving only a lingering hint of very expensive perfume behind her.

Ginny stood as if fixed to the spot, tears stinging at her eyes. It couldn't be true... Could it? And yet... Ever since Oliver had asked her to marry him she had been struggling to understand what on earth a man like him could possibly see in her; after all, he wasn't far off thirty, successful, well-travelled—while she was barely out of school. And he hadn't ever actually *said* he loved her—not in so many words...

Weakly she sat down on the edge of the bed, staring bleakly at her own reflection in the mirror above the dressing table. Was that it? Was he marrying her simply so that she could provide him with a Marsden heir, in due course to take over his seat at the bank? An heir that Alina couldn't give him.

Alina... How could she ever have let herself think she could compete with that incomparable creature? It wasn't just her beauty and elegance which set her above her more ordinary sisters; it was that air of refinement, of sophistication—the ability to tell a Monet from a Matisse, a Meursault from a Montrachet. And it was in her ability to captivate a man and hold him in thrall. Witness the enraptured expression of the man she had been talking to downstairs—for him, there had been no one else in the room.

But it was no good sitting here crying like a fool, she chided herself sternly. She had to speak to Oliver—she had to know the truth. And she had to do it with dignity—however difficult that would be. Pausing for just a moment to repair the damage caused by those acid tears, she drew in a few deep, steadying breaths, and then opened the door and walked resolutely down the stairs.

The party was in full swing, but she couldn't see Oliver—or Alina. Someone spoke to her, and she responded automatically with a smile. 'Have you seen Oliver?'

'I think he was out on the terrace a moment ago.'

'Thank you…'

Her stomach tied up in knots, she slipped out through the open French windows onto the wide terrace that ran along the back of the house. There was no sign of Oliver… But as she hesitated, wondering whether to walk on into the garden to look for him, she heard voices—quiet voices, close by.

They were in the shadows at the far end of the terrace, beneath the wisteria. The man had his back to her, but she knew it was Oliver—she could never mistake the set of those wide shoulders, the well-shaped dark head. And there could be no doubting the identity of the woman in his arms as the moonlight caught an answering gleam from her silver-blonde hair.

'Of course it won't make any difference,' she heard him say, softly but quite distinctly. 'Nothing will ever change between us…'

Ginny stepped back sharply, stunned by such unequivocal proof, stumbling as her foot caught on a loose flagstone. Oliver turned, his expression of surprise as he saw her there quickly replaced by one of annoyance. Alina moved smoothly out of his arms, her smile that of a cat who had lapped up the cream. 'Excuse me,' she murmured, and discreetly slipped away, leaving them alone.

Oliver frowned, glancing from where Alina had disappeared back to Ginny. 'What's the matter?' he demanded.

'What do you mean, what's the matter?' Ginny countered, half choking on her tears. 'What were you doing out here with *her?*'

His dark eyes glittered in warning. 'What exactly do you mean by that?' he enquired tautly.

'What do you think I mean?' she threw at him, all her plans for a dignified discussion blown to the four winds. She wanted to shout at him, scream at him, but she was forced to keep her voice quiet so as not to attract unwelcome attention. 'You're supposed to be engaged to me, but ever since she came back to England with you, you seem to have preferred to spend your time with *her!*'

'So?' His voice was sharp with irritation. 'She's my stepsister, for goodness' sake! And she's been going through a difficult time recently. I told you, you can't expect me to dance attention on you all the time, so you'd better get used to it and not start behaving like a spoiled brat!'

Ginny drew in a sharp breath, as if she had been slapped in the face. 'A spoiled brat? Is that what you think of me?' she demanded. Tears were stinging her eyes as she tugged at the ring, her beautiful emerald ring that had been on her finger for barely an hour. 'Well, in that case you'd better have this back!' And, throwing it at his feet, she turned and ran, down the steps of the terrace and across the lawn, to lose herself in the shadows of the garden.

Blinded by her tears, she wandered along the neatly kept gravel paths until she found herself at the side of the house, where the guests had parked their cars. Oliver's car was there—he had hired an Aston Martin again, as he had that day when he had picked her up from school for half term. She stroked her hand along the gleaming wing, reliving every moment of that brief drive. She had told herself then that he could never be interested in a naïve little schoolgirl; she should have listened to her own advice.

The sound of unsteady footsteps on the gravel behind her made her turn in some alarm. But it was only Mark Ransome—more than a little drunk, as usual, his dark Byronic curls disordered, his well-cut dinner jacket hanging loosely open. He peered at her, recognising her in the shadows, and grinned.

'Ah—it's Ginny! Hello, old thing. Great party!' He hiccuped. ''Scuse me—got a little hog-tied, I'm afraid.'

She returned him a wan smile. She had known Mark for years; he had often declared himself to be madly in love with her, but she never took him seriously—he had declared the same thing to at least half a dozen of her friends. 'You weren't planning to drive home in that state, were you?' she enquired with some concern—it would be just like Mark to act so irresponsibly.

'No, no—just come out for a breath of air,' he assured her, blinking as he tried to focus both his eyes on her at the same time. 'Well, so you're off the market, eh? Always was a lucky bastard, old Ollie Marsden! Might have known he'd snap you up before any of the rest of us got a look in!' He sighed heavily, leaning closer towards her, favouring her with his somewhat whisky-soaked breath. 'Always fancied you a bit myself, you know. Can't blame you for turning me down, though. Bad lot, and all that—too fond of the sauce. Runs in the family! Tell you what, though, you're the prettiest of the lot. Trust Ollie to spot that.'

'Yes, well...' Her jaw was clenched taut. 'I'm not going to marry him, Mark. I hate him!'

Mark frowned, his fuddled mind slowly taking in this

surprising information. 'Not going to marry him?' he
protested. 'But you just got engaged to him.'

'And promptly got un-engaged,' she asserted bitterly.
'It must have been just about the shortest engagement in
history.' The tears welled up and she leaned towards
him, simply seeking comfort. 'Oh, Mark...!'

Apparently not knowing what else to do, he wrapped
his arms around her and patted her hair. 'Oh...! Well,
but... Come on, old girl. I mean...'

She lifted her head, looking up at him. He was really
quite good-looking—when he wasn't too drunk. A lot of
the girls fancied him, in spite of—or more likely because
of—his rakish reputation. And, after all, what was sauce
for the goose was sauce for the gander! 'Kiss me, Mark,'
she commanded recklessly.

He looked momentarily startled, but he didn't argue.
Closing her eyes, she tilted up her face, parting her lips
as his mouth came down on hers.

Actually he kissed quite nicely—apart from the taste
of whisky. Not like Oliver, of course... But she wasn't
even going to think about Oliver ever again. Reaching
up her arms, she wrapped them tightly around Mark's
neck, drawing him down to her. Encouraged, his hands
began to wander in a way that she would have swiftly
slapped down under normal circumstances. But tonight
she didn't care—she'd do as she damned well liked!

'Let's get in the car,' he mumbled thickly.

Yes! Oh, wouldn't that just serve Oliver right? If she
should lose the cherished virginity she had been saving
for him in the back of his own car! The door wasn't
locked, and she opened it quickly and they both fell onto
the back seat in a tumble of arms and legs. Mark was
breathing hard, fumbling to find the zip of her dress, his
mouth wet and sloppy over her face.

It was awkward and cramped in the back of the car,

and Ginny was already beginning to regret her impulsive action. But Mark was full of enthusiasm now, pulling her back across his lap and trapping her in the corner of the seat, slobbering kisses over her neck and shoulders. She tried to shift him a little, to ease her uncomfortable position, but he took that as further encouragement and put his hand down to slide it up beneath the hem of her skirt.

'Mark... Please...' she whispered, struggling to pull her dress back up over her shoulder at the same time as fending him off with the other hand. 'I don't think perhaps we should...'

She felt something snag, and he muttered a curse. 'Damn—I've caught my cufflink on your stupid tights!' he grumbled, bending his head to examine the cause of the problem. In his drunken state he toppled over onto the driver's seat, his elbow becoming wedged against the steering wheel—setting off the horn.

'Oh, no...!' In a panic, Ginny tried to twist free, succeeding only in rucking her skirt up still further—and at that moment the door of the car was wrenched open.

All Ginny saw was Alina, a smile of grim triumph on her face. Behind her, a circle of interested observers were trying to catch a glimpse of what was going on. The evidence was damning: her hair was wildly tousled, her dress had slipped halfway off her shoulders—and Mark's hand was resting high on one exposed thigh.

'Ginny! What on earth...?' Alina's voice conveyed the most profound shock. 'How *could* you?'

Ginny felt herself blush the deepest shade of scarlet. Scrabbling to lift the strap of her dress back onto her shoulder, she snatched Mark's hand from her leg, ripping her tights, and stumbled out of the car. And ran—away from all those witnesses to her shame—around the side of the house and in through the kitchen door, up the back stairs and into her bedroom, where she locked the door and threw herself on the bed, vowing she wouldn't come out again for a hundred years...

Was it really so long ago? Dancing with Oliver now, held close against that lean, hard-muscled body, breathing the musky male scent of his skin, it would have been easy to pretend that those years had never been—that they were dancing at their engagement party and his ring was still on her finger.

But the past couldn't be so easily erased, she mused bitterly. That night had cast a very long shadow.

From beneath her lashes, she was able to study Oliver's face—the hard line of his jaw, the uncompromising set of his mouth. She had never really known how he had reacted to the scandal. She had sent him a polite little note of apology, suggesting that he should keep the ring, and by the time she had emerged from her self-imposed internment he had returned to America.

And she had found that the gossips had been having a field-day over the incident. Mark had been an unfortunate choice of accomplice. Those who had witnessed the scene hadn't been quite sure what they had seen, but had been more than ready to fill in the gaps—and the story had lost nothing in the telling. Mark's rather vague denials had been brushed aside—in truth, he had been rather too drunk to remember very clearly what had happened. Alina was the only one who could have redeemed Ginny's reputation—but she had let her silence speak volumes.

At first she hadn't really cared what people said of her—being thought a little wild had seemed like an excellent disguise for a broken heart. And it had soon become apparent that there was nothing much she could do about it anyway—she only had to dance with a young

man at a party for his name to be added to the growing
list of her supposed lovers and one-night stands.

And, regrettably, her partners had frequently proved
not to be the gentlemen she might have been entitled to
expect them to be—too afraid of the mockery of their
peers if they were thought to be the only one who hadn't
got past first base with her. So now here she was, sad-
dled with a reputation quite as rakish as Mark's had ever
been—and with not an ounce of justification.

As for Alina—she had won; game, set and match. Or
so it had seemed at the time. The doubts had crept in
slowly. After all, if Oliver was really in love with her,
why hadn't he simply married her? Even if modern
medical treatment couldn't deal with her inability to
have children, they could always adopt. It was a much
more logical solution than the Gothic plot Alina had
drawn for her.

If she'd had a crumb of sense, of course, she would
have realised that at the time, instead of reacting so hot-
headedly. But she had been young and unsure of herself,
over-excited by her romantic dreams—all too easy for a
woman like Alina to manipulate. Nowadays she would
be more of a match for her.

But it was too late now, she reminded herself wryly—
much too late. What good was there in letting herself
wonder about what might have been? If Oliver had ever
felt anything for her, it had all long ago turned sour.
And now, after all this time, he had decided that the
conditions were right to exact his revenge—a dish best
served, as they said, ice-cold.

A cool breeze shivered around her shoulders, drawing
her back out of her thoughts. How long had they been
dancing? The moon, which when she had first come out
here had been sailing like a silver dollar high in the
velvet sky, had disappeared, leaving only the distant

stars. The band was still playing, but through a gap in
the curtains she could see that the ballroom was almost
empty; a few couples were dancing among the drifting,
half-deflated balloons and tangled swirls of streamers,
and a few more were sitting at the tables as the staff
moved discreetly around, clearing away the debris of
supper.

'Oh...I didn't realise it was getting so late,' she remarked, stifling a yawn.

Oliver twisted his wrist to glance at his slim gold
watch. 'You don't have too long to go if you're really
planning to dance till dawn,' he confirmed dryly.

She smiled a little crookedly, shaking her head. 'Oh,
I don't think I'll bother, after all. It can become a bit of
a bore if you do it all the time.'

He laughed, lazily mocking. 'Perhaps you're getting
a little too old to keep playing the wild child?' he suggested.

'Oh, no.' She shook her head decisively. 'I shall go
on being a wild child until I'm old enough to be an
outrageous old lady.'

'And I used to think you were such a sweet little innocent,' he taunted softly. 'A virgin bride. How mistaken I was—so concerned for your maidenly virtue, so
careful not to frighten you...' His hand had slid slowly
up her arm and across her shoulder, and now it was
around her throat, forcing her head back. 'But I needn't
have bothered, need I? Perhaps if I'd been a little less
gallant you wouldn't have felt the need to go romping
around half-naked in the back of my car with some
drunken Lothario too addled to appreciate the pleasures
you were handing out so liberally.'

At last he had unveiled the raw anger he had kept
concealed for so long beneath that urbane exterior, and
as his fingers tightened around her throat she drew in

her breath on a sharp stab of panic. For a fleeting moment she thought he was going to strangle her... But then his mouth came down on hers, hard and insistent, crushing her lips apart, forcing her to yield to the plundering invasion of his tongue as it swirled into all the deepest corners of her mouth, demanding her surrender.

It wasn't a kiss—it was a punishment. At least, that was what he had intended. But the pure savagery of it seemed to ignite her mercurial spirit, the flames fuelled by all the pain and heartache of the past six years, and suddenly she was kissing him back, not caring that he was bruising her lips, matching his fierce urgency with her own.

His hand was in the small of her back, curving her hard against him, and as she dragged raggedly for breath the tight constraint of the whalebone in her dress was crushing her breasts, the abrasion of the fabric against the tender peaks sending sparks of fire into her brain. If he had kissed her like this before she would never have let Alina or anyone else take him away from her...

At long last he drew back, a mocking glint in those dark eyes. 'Well—you've certainly learned a thing or two since the last time I kissed you,' he remarked—and his tone did not imply that it was a compliment.

It gave her some sort of bitter satisfaction to meet his gaze, her head tilted at a defiant angle. 'It would be a little surprising if I hadn't,' she retorted, managing with an effort of will to put up her usual flippant façade. 'Six years is a long time. I didn't spend it in a convent.'

'No, I don't suppose you did.' He laughed coldly. 'In fact if even a quarter of the things I've heard about you are true, you seem to have come close to spending it in a bordello!'

Her soft mouth curved into a saucy smile. 'Listening to gossip, Oliver? Shame on you!'

'Oh, I never rely purely on second-hand information,' he countered, an inflection of sardonic humour in his voice. 'I always try to conduct my own…research.' With the pad of his thumb he traced the outline of her trembling lips, still tender from his bruising kiss. 'I think the evidence confirms the market rumours,' he taunted softly.

'Well, don't think you'll be adding me to your portfolio,' she retorted acidly. 'You've bought me for one day, and one day is all you're going to get.' And, turning him an aloof shoulder, she walked back into the ballroom.

CHAPTER FIVE

THE restaurant was new, and very smart; the food was excellent, and her date was pleasant enough company. But though she genuinely tried her best, Ginny just couldn't summon up any kind of enthusiasm.

It was almost a week now since the night of the charity ball, and her money worries hadn't gone away. An uncomfortable discussion with her father's solicitor had brought her to the dispiriting conclusion that there was little chance of her being able to salvage anything at all from the wreckage. Another demand was due shortly, and to meet it she was going to have to sell the house.

Under such desperate circumstances, Sara's light-hearted suggestion that she should find herself a rich husband was beginning to seem like the only serious option. Of course, she couldn't ever consider marrying someone she didn't like, but that still left her quite a large field to choose from.

Or so it had seemed—until this evening.

Oh, Jeremy was nice enough—but, as Sara had said, he was too nice. He had been all attentiveness, anxious to do whatever she wanted, never disagreeing with a single thing she said—even when, out of sheer exasperation, she had deliberately contradicted herself.

And, just to add the finishing touch, as the waiter was serving their main course she had chanced to glance casually around the room—and had found herself gazing straight into Oliver's dark, mocking eyes. He was dining alone; she hadn't noticed him come in, but then she hadn't noticed him when they had arrived, either—if she had, she might have suggested to Jeremy that they should go somewhere else.

Damn—why did he have to choose *this* restaurant, out of all the ones he could have picked? It had to be mere coincidence...didn't it? She had done her best to ignore him, but she was much too conscious of him, watching her with that dark, steady gaze—it had ruined her appetite.

'Would you like some more wine?' Jeremy enquired diffidently, picking up the bottle.

'Thank you.' She forced a smile, holding out her glass for him to pour—but in his nervousness he let a little of it splash over her hand.

'Oh... Oh, dear, I'm sorry...'

'It's all right.' She hadn't meant to let that taut note of irritation creep into her voice, but her patience, already strained by the events of the past couple of weeks, was at breaking point.

'I'm sorry,' he said, flustered. 'Here...' He offered her his napkin to dry her hand—but she had already used her own. 'I'm sorry...'

'And for goodness' sake will you stop apologising?'

'I'm sorry...' Poor Jeremy subsided into an abject heap, gazing at her with the hurt eyes of a whipped puppy.

She forced herself to bite her tongue—she was behaving like an absolute bitch, and it wasn't Jeremy's fault. Just count to ten and smile, she told herself, struggling with the impulse to get hold of him and give him a good shake. 'It doesn't matter...'

'Good evening.'

She glanced up sharply to find Oliver standing beside their table, the mocking glint in his dark eyes warning her that he had heard most of the past few minutes' exchange.

Jeremy's open face lit with relief. 'Oliver! Well, this is a pleasant surprise, isn't it, Ginny? Why don't you...? I mean, unless you're with someone else, of course. We've almost finished our dinner. Sit down—have a glass of wine with us. That is...' He turned to Ginny, his eyes pleading for a release from the discomfort of being alone with her.

She conceded a wry smile; had she really been so horrid?

Oliver accepted the invitation with a polite inclination of his head; the head waiter himself was already bringing a third chair to their table.

'So, what do you think of the place?' Jeremy asked, eager to please. 'I bumped into Oliver at the squash club yesterday and he asked me if there was anywhere I could recommend,' he added proudly to Ginny. 'I told him we were coming here tonight.'

Only long practice of concealing her emotions enabled her to maintain her cool façade; her mind was in turmoil. She should have known it was no mere unlucky coincidence that had brought Oliver to the same restaurant. Just happened to bump into Jeremy? Just happened to ask him casually to recommend a restaurant? Yes, and pigs might fly. Poor Jeremy had probably never even realised that he was being duped.

The question was—why?

'Well, now, isn't this nice?' Jeremy's forced jollity served only to exacerbate her own tension. 'Shall we get another bottle of wine in?' He raised his hand, waving to try to attract the attention of one of the waiters.

Oliver shook his head. 'Not for me, thank you—I'll just have a coffee.' He seemed to do no more than raise one dark eyebrow a millimetre or two, but a waiter was instantly at his side; the contrast with Jeremy's unsuccessful efforts was almost embarrassing.

'So... How's Lady Lulworth?' Jeremy enquired brightly.

Oliver conceded a smile of dry humour. 'Very well, I believe. I have to confess that I'm rather doing my best to keep out of her way.'

Jeremy laughed a little too loudly. 'Don't blame you! Terrifies me, that woman. Reminds me of an old aunt of mine—lives in some dreadful draughty old place in Northumberland. Have to go up a couple of times a year, just to make sure she doesn't leave her pile to an old cats' home or something. Cats! She's got dozens of 'em, slinking about, jumping on your bed in the middle of the night. Could give you a nasty turn, that kind of thing...'

At least with Jeremy babbling on there was no need for Ginny to make conversation with Oliver. The waiter had brought her dessert, and she sat picking at it, struggling to still the uncomfortable awareness of the man at her side. But somehow the memory of the way he had kissed her at the ball kept replaying itself in her brain, and she found herself studying again that firmly drawn, sensual mouth, an odd little ache tugging inside her. She must be completely crazy, but she couldn't deny it—she wanted him to kiss her again.

The evening was spiralling rapidly from difficult to disastrous. Unfortunately Jeremy, to cope with his awkwardness, was drinking far too much, his face flushed, his speech increasingly rambling and slurred. By the time they left the restaurant it was obvious that he was far too drunk to drive.

'Can I offer you a lift?' Oliver suggested, holding open the door for Ginny as she discreetly shepherded Jeremy through it, virtually holding him up when he staggered as the cool night air clashed with the alcohol in his bloodstream.

'Oh... No, thank you—we wouldn't dream of putting you to such inconvenience,' she responded quickly—the very last thing she wanted was to be in his company for any longer than was absolutely necessary.

The sardonic glint in his eyes mocked her cowardice. 'Do you really think he's in a fit state to go home in a taxi?' he taunted lazily.

She hesitated, her head still tilted up at a defiant angle. But he was absolutely right, damn him—Jeremy could barely stand. She was going to have considerable difficulty getting him safely home. 'Very well, then,' she conceded tersely. 'Thank you.'

He raised his hand and a sleek dark blue Rolls Royce which had been waiting a few hundred yards up the road swept elegantly down to meet them. A uniformed chauffeur climbed out, his face wooden at the sight of Jeremy, who was swaying slightly on his feet, gazing blearily up at the moon.

'We'll be making a short diversion, Foster,' Oliver informed him dryly.

'Yes, sir. Er...the gentleman wouldn't be likely to be feeling a little...queasy in the back of the car, would he, sir?'

'I sincerely hope not,' Oliver responded, conceding a grim smile. 'If it should seem imminent, I shall attempt to warn you in time.'

'Thank you, sir,' the chauffeur responded, clearly concerned for the welfare of his precious vehicle.

It was only with some difficulty that they managed to persuade Jeremy not to start quoting poetry to the moon and get into the back of the car. He clambered in awkwardly, sprawling across the back seat—where he promptly fell asleep. Oliver climbed in beside him, taking his weight and propping him against his shoulder. Ginny, excruciatingly embarrassed at the drunken condition of her date, could only accept the chauffeur's polite suggestion that she should use the other door.

At least it was fairly dark in the back of the car. From beneath her lashes, Ginny was able to study Oliver's hard profile. What sort of game was he playing, turning up like that at the restaurant where Jeremy had taken her, watching her with those dark, disturbing eyes, making her feel like a very small mouse being hunted by a large and predatory cat? Was it his way of warning her that there could be no escape from the retribution he had planned for her?

If so, she wasn't going to let him know how much he had succeeded in unsettling her. Pinning her best social smile in place, she sought for a neutral topic of conversation. 'So, how do you like being back in London?' she queried pleasantly.

His faintly mocking smile conveyed a mild amusement at her efforts. 'I'm getting used to it,' he drawled lazily. 'The pace of life is quite a bit slower, of course, but that's no bad thing. It gives me time to think about...things other than work.'

'Well, that's good.' She was struggling for a light touch of humour, but even to her own ears it sounded strained. 'Too much work and no play isn't good for your health!'

'How would you know that?' he taunted, a sardonic inflection in his voice. 'You've never done a day's work in your life.'

She acknowledged the accusation with a dismissive shrug of her slender shoulders. 'Why should I want a job?' she returned airily. 'I don't need the money.'

'Don't you?' He was lounging back in the corner of the seat, his dark eyes in shadow, but she could sense him watching her, a faintly sardonic smile curving the corners of his hard mouth. 'So what are you planning to do now that your father's estate has been wiped out? Find yourself a wealthy husband? Someone who can afford to keep you in the style you think you deserve?'

For a moment she felt as though she was choking. 'H-How did you know about my father's estate?' she demanded defensively.

'My father told me, naturally. How long did you think you could keep it quiet? Just long enough to lure some poor bedazzled fool to the altar? When were you planning to tell him? On your wedding night? Not a very sound basis for a successful marriage, I would have thought.'

'Don't be…ridiculous,' she retorted uncomfortably. 'As if I'd even consider doing a thing like that!'

He laughed, softly mocking. 'You wouldn't? You mean the idea has never even crossed your mind?'

Ginny felt a hot blush of scarlet colour her cheeks. But fortunately at that moment the car slid to a halt at the kerb outside Jeremy's flat, saving her from the necessity of finding a response.

Jeremy grunted as they shook him awake, drunkenly amiable and convinced that Oliver was his life-long best friend. It took all Oliver's and his chauffeur's best efforts to coax him out of the car, and then he stood on the pavement, his arm looped around Oliver's neck, blinking questioningly up at the building beside which they stood.

'Where're we goin'?' he slurred. 'Hey, it's my place! I say—that's jolly! Why don't you all come in for a li'l nightcap, eh?'

'I think perhaps you ought to stick to coffee,' Oliver advised him dampeningly. 'Preferably black.'

It took all three of them to get him safely inside the flat, and once there it was a struggle to dissuade him from raiding his well-stocked drinks cabinet. But at last they managed to coax him to bed. Ginny removed his shoes as Oliver deftly stripped him of his jacket and tie, and they left him snoring peacefully on top of the duvet.

Back in the car, Ginny heaved a sigh of relief—and then flushed as she caught the sardonic glint in Oliver's dark eyes.

'What on earth are you dating that young idiot for?' he queried, an inflection of mocking humour in his voice.

She tilted up her chin, struggling to retain some semblance of dignity. 'I'll date who I like,' she retorted. 'I don't have to ask for your approval.'

'You're not really planning to marry him, are you?'

'What if I am?' she countered stiffly. 'It's none of your business whom I choose to marry.'

He laughed softly, shaking his head. 'The poor sap! No, Ginny—you can't do it. You'd make his life a misery.'

She risked slanting him a brief glance, arching one finely drawn eyebrow in cool question. 'Why should you care?' she demanded tautly. 'It's not as if he's a particular friend of yours.'

Those dark eyes glinted with sardonic amusement. 'Let's just say I don't like to witness cruelty to helpless creatures,' he responded, lazily provocative. 'Do you think you could even be faithful to him for more than a week?'

She shrugged her slim shoulders in a gesture of careless dismissal. It hurt that he had accepted so readily the unjust reputation she had earned, but she had no intention of trying to disabuse him. 'I doubt it,' she retorted lightly.

'So why marry him?'

'I never said I was going to,' she protested, frustrated that she seemed to have so little control over the conversation. 'I just said it was none of your business.'

'Oh, but it is.' There was a soft note of menace beneath that silky-smooth voice. 'I wouldn't want people to think you'd prefer to marry a wet fish like that than marry me.'

She forced a laugh, shaking her head. 'Oh, I very much doubt that anyone would think that,' she asserted blithely. 'Most people will have forgotten all about that ill-matched engagement by now—it was all such a long time ago.'

'Do you really think so?'

No, she didn't. It had been a particularly juicy piece of scandal—she was only too well aware that no one had forgotten any of it.

He reached across and twisted his finger into one loose coil of her hair. 'You should have married me, you know.' His voice was a smoky murmur. 'Then you wouldn't have been reduced to going out with the likes of Jeremy.'

She caught her breath so sharply she almost choked. He was laughing, mocking her, his eyes impossible to read. It took every ounce of will-power she possessed to return him a look of frosty disdain. 'For...your information,' she returned tautly, 'we were going along very well until you intruded.'

'It didn't look like it,' he taunted. 'You looked bored out of your skull.'

'It's just that you're so arrogant you can't imagine how a woman could have a good time with anyone else but you!' she rapped, angry with herself for letting him goad her.

'Arrogant?' He thought that one over, and appeared to decide it was a compliment. 'Possibly. But if you went out to dinner with me, I can assure you you wouldn't be bored. And if you had married me, you would never have been unfaithful.'

'Oh?' Her heart was beating much too fast. 'What would you have done? Kept me locked up in the attic?'

'No.' He leaned forward and snapped down the blind that separated them from the driver's seat—leaving them alone in their private world of luxury in the back of the elegant car. 'I would simply have made sure that you never wanted to make love with anyone else.'

Suddenly Ginny found herself trapped in the corner of the seat. With one hand he brushed a wayward strand of hair back from her cheek, a slow smile curving that intriguingly sensual mouth as she stared up at him, struggling to resist the temptation to let herself drown in the depths of those dark, dangerous eyes.

'Ever...' he asserted, his voice low and husky as his mouth brushed over hers.

His kiss was tender, tantalising, promising a sweet intimacy that was all she had ever dreamed of. As she let go her breath on a soundless sigh he took the soft curve of her lower lip between his hard white teeth, nibbling at it sensuously, sending erotic shivers along her quivering nerve-fibres.

Every warning voice inside her head was shrieking at her to resist, but something was melting inside her, undermining all her defences; she was surrendering helplessly to the magic of his spell as his languorous tongue swirled over the delicate inner membranes of her lips, inciting her response.

His arms were around her, drawing her closer against him, and she shivered as she sensed the raw male strength in him, so smoothly concealed beneath that urbane manner and immaculately tailored City suit. His hand had slid down the length of her body, claiming an intimacy she knew she should deny him, but she didn't know how.

A deep, aching need had stirred inside her—a need

that he had first awoken so many years ago, on that magical night when she had first danced with him, the night of her nineteenth birthday. She had thought she had learned to control it, but now it was gnawing at her with a fierce urgency—and, like a genie escaped from a bottle, she knew she would never be able to control it again.

His kiss deepened, plundering every sweet, secret corner of her mouth as her head tipped back into the crook of his arm, helpless in surrender. She knew that her weakness would only fuel his contempt, seeming to confirm that all those stories about her were true. How would he know that there had been no one—nothing more than a few kisses? None of which had kindled so much as a candle-glow inside her. Nothing like this.

Slowly, tantalisingly, his hand was moving up, stroking over the slender length of her thigh, past her slim waist... Her breath seemed to stay in her throat as she waited, taut with anticipation, until at last his fingers brushed against the ripe curve of her breast, cupping it as if to assess its firm ripeness, moulding it caressingly, crushing it beneath his palm. She felt the tender peak harden into a sweet bud of pleasure, sizzling beneath that delicious abrasion, and her spine curled in pleasure as she moved invitingly against him, moaning softly as she sought wantonly for more of his exquisite touch...

'You're not going to marry Jeremy,' he growled fiercely. 'Nor any of those other trust-fund wimps you've been dating. If you're going to marry anyone, it's going to be me.'

Her eyes flew open in shock. Some kind of crooked smile quirked his hard mouth, but it conveyed no trace of warmth or humour. He still held her trapped in the corner of the seat, his hand still lingering on her breast with a ruthless possessiveness that warned her of the true intent behind his words.

'No…!' She struggled to push him away, retreating as far as she could into her own corner of the seat. 'Marry you? You must be crazy!'

He laughed in lazy mockery, sliding back along the seat into his own corner. 'Is that such a horrific prospect?' he queried dryly. 'You didn't appear to think so six years ago.'

She shrugged her slender shoulders, conjuring all her skills of deception to match his air of cool detachment. 'I was…flattered,' she returned, risking a note of flippancy. 'I *was* only nineteen, you know. The trouble was, my father insisted on that stupid party, inviting everyone, and I really didn't know how to get out of it.'

'I appreciate your dilemma.' His voice was smooth with menace. 'Unfortunately I have a rooted dislike of allowing anyone to renege on a promise.'

'You're not serious,' she protested a little unsteadily, watching him as if he was a panther ready to strike. 'After…everything that happened?'

His dark eyes glinted with chilling humour. 'Ah, yes—you have rather a taste for making love in the back of cars, don't you?' he mused. 'It was quite a scene, from what I heard. But Mark Ransome? Really, I would have thought you had better taste.'

'At least he was a little closer to my own age,' she retorted, striking out at him in desperation. 'And fun to be with.'

Her poison dart missed its mark. He merely smiled, a smile of lazy arrogance. 'It promises to be an interesting game,' he taunted. 'But be warned—I have a reputation for always getting what I want. And to earn a reputation like that sometimes you have to play a little rough.'

Ginny felt her heartbeat pounding. He had already

given her one demonstration of just how rough he was willing to play, ruthlessly exploiting her body's treacherous weakness for his kisses, his expert caresses. The rational part of her mind might be fully aware of the sweet trap, but she wasn't at all sure that she could resist the bait.

The car had stopped at some traffic lights, and suddenly she realised that they were just a few hundred yards from her door. Her one instinctive thought was to escape. 'Th-Thank you for the lift,' she rapped out, fumbling for the door-catch. 'I can walk from here.' And, favouring him with a smile which she hoped conveyed a great deal more assurance than she felt, she stepped from the car and walked briskly away.

'Ginny...?'

She tilted up her chin at a haughty angle, ignoring him...an effect that was somewhat ruined when she realised that she had left her handbag in the car. As she turned it drew level with her, and the dark-tinted window slid silently down. A hand held the bag out to her, and from the shadows his eyes glinted with sardonic amusement.

'Thank you,' she grated tautly, almost snatching it from him.

'Sleep well.'

The window slid up and the elegant car purred away from the kerb, turning right towards the City.

Sleep? Ginny sighed, and punched the pillow into a more comfortable shape. She couldn't imagine that she would ever be able to sleep again. The clock on her bedside table taunted her with the unwanted information that it was twenty-five minutes past four—it must have been at least two hours since the last time she had looked at it, and it had been just twenty past four then.

Only a few short weeks ago life had been quite simple and straightforward. She had been perfectly happy…well, as happy as most people, anyway. And she had more or less assumed that the world would continue in much the same way—maybe even that one day she might marry one of the nice young men who courted her so eagerly.

But all those comfortable illusions had been shattered now, she acknowledged wryly—and not just because of her dire financial crisis. She had really known all along that she could never marry anyone but Oliver, could never share another man's bed.

But she couldn't marry Oliver, either. A hot shiver ran through her as she recalled that scene in the back of his car, the dark glint of warning in his eyes as he had spoken, the insolently possessive way his hand had lingered on her breast…

With a small groan she turned her heated face into the pillow. She must have been crazy to let things go as far as that; all it had done was confirm for him that everything that had been said about her was true—that she was easy with her favours, that she deserved his contempt. But if he felt like that, why on earth did he want to marry her?

Did she even have to ask? Six years ago she had trampled on his pride, and now he wanted more than mere revenge—he wanted restitution. By forcing her to marry him he could to some extent wipe out the memory of that past affront—but if she married someone else, it would only reinforce it.

But what sort of marriage would it be? He had demonstrated with devastating clarity in the way he had kissed her, the way he had touched her, that it would be no mere façade. He was going to demand her total surrender. And she was all too aware of how easily he could sweep aside her defences. Her mind might struggle to resist, but her traitorous body would betray her.

Even now, in spite of every argument the rational part of her might present, she ached for him, with a deep, gnawing hunger that wouldn't go away. How much worse would it be if she had to share his bed every night—or at least, as often as he wanted her there? Because she was under no illusion—once he was sated on the spoils of victory, there would be nothing left. But he wouldn't let her go—oh, no, he would keep her tied to him, for ever.

And as part of her marital duties, no doubt, he would expect her to present him with an heir.

A sudden sharp pain stabbed through her. To be pregnant by him, to bear his child... She had dreamed about it once, vague romantic imaginings of wriggling pink babies, of chubby toddlers with big dark eyes just like his... But she had forced herself to put all those dreams away, with the others, and never to acknowledge even the slightest twinge of envy when any of her friends had proudly announced their pregnancy or shown off their brand new bundle of joy to be cooed over.

It had fitted quite neatly with her image, of course: Ginny Hamilton, the frivolous social butterfly, selfish and shallow—babies could ruin your figure, and small children were so demanding, leaving their toys all over the place and getting their sticky fingers on your things. No one was in the least bit surprised that she showed no interest in them.

Something seemed to be stinging at the back of her eyes, and she realised with some surprise that it was a tear. It was a very long time since she had let herself cry. Even her father's death, coming as it had after a long illness, had produced sadness but no real tears. So why should she cry over stupid Oliver Marsden? It wasn't as if she was still in love with him...

Yes, dammit, she was. Or at least she was in love with the Oliver Marsden she remembered from New York—the laughing companion who had taken her out on the Staten Island Ferry, pointing out to her all the landmarks of Manhattan, who had raced her up the spiral steps of the Guggenheim Museum, and eaten ice-creams with her in Battery Park.

Okay, she had been young and impressionable then, but it was difficult to believe that she had been totally wrong about him. Maybe it was true that he hadn't been in love with her the way she had wanted him to be— maybe he *had* asked her to marry him out of some odd sort of loyalty to his father, and a desire to have a son to carry on his family name. But he could have come to love her eventually—if Alina hadn't interfered in the way she had.

But there was no chance now that that spirit could ever be recaptured—she had destroyed it with her foolish, impetuous behaviour that night. All that was left was an angry, hostile man, set on punishing her—and she really couldn't blame him. But as she slipped into restless dreams the words that whispered in her head were, If only...

CHAPTER SIX

THE house seemed to echo with emptiness. Ginny wandered from room to room, memories swirling around her—happy memories of her childhood, of her mother... Of coming home from a walk on a wet spring morning, laughing as they tugged off their wellingtons here in the hall, as Buster the springer spaniel—who was now buried in the shade of the lilac tree in the garden—shook himself and sprayed them both liberally with muddy water. Memories of nestling down into the corner of one of the big, squashy chintz-covered sofas here in the yellow room to watch Children's Hour on the television— this was the only room where a television had been allowed to intrude.

One tear trickled slowly down her cheek, but she didn't bother to brush it aside. She had forced herself to accept that she was going to have to sell, but she hadn't expected that a buyer would be found so quickly. The market for large houses like this wasn't particularly buoyant at the moment, so she had hoped to have at least a little more time. Although she hadn't actually lived here for the past three or four years, it was still her home.

She found herself already bitterly resenting the unknown buyer she had come here to meet. Someone else would be gazing out of these tall French windows onto the sunny garden, someone who would probably choose to change the faded Regency-stripe wallpaper and throw out the old-fashioned brocade curtains. If indeed they were even planning to live here at all. What if it was the representative of some anonymous corporation she was to meet, who was planning to turn the house into a conference centre or a health farm, or to root up the woods and lay out a golf course?

A small frown creased her brow. Was that the reason why the estate agent had been so reticent? Unfortunately she had no choice in the matter—she was obliged to accept the highest offer that was made.

The sound of a car crunching over the gravel drive brought her head around. They had arrived—punctual to the minute. Her time here alone was over; her last goodbyes had been said. Drawing in a deep, steadying breath, she walked across the room and out to the lofty woodpanelled hall. She had decided that she would seize the initiative by opening the front door before her visitor had rung the bell—standing at the top of the steps would give her the advantage of height.

But the advantage didn't last beyond the time it took her to recognise the sleek elegance of the long-nosed Aston Martin parked by the rose bed, or the tall man climbing out from behind the steering wheel. Oliver Marsden. Her heart gave a sharp thump, and began to race much too fast. 'What are you doing here?' she demanded belligerently.

He climbed the steps with an easy, athletic stride, arriving beside her so that she was forced to look up at him. 'That's not a very gracious way to welcome a potential buyer,' he taunted, a glint of dark amusement in his eyes. 'Especially one who's ready to make a very generous offer.'

'*You?*' Dammit, she should have guessed; he had warned her that he played rough. 'What do you want with my house?'

He shrugged those wide shoulders in a casual gesture. 'Now that I'm settling permanently in England, I want a place to live,' he responded blandly. 'So, are you going to show me around?'

'You don't need to see around,' she retorted, returning him an icy glare. 'You know the house—you've visited it often enough.'

The mocking glint in his dark eyes challenged her attempts at evasion. 'I'd like to look around anyway,' he insisted. 'If it's not too much trouble?'

She hesitated, struggling with the temptation to slam the door in his face. 'All right,' she conceded tersely. 'You'd better come in, then.'

'Thank you.'

Forced into retreat, she could only hide behind a façade of cool dignity. After all, the house had to be sold—it really made very little difference who it was sold to. The outcome would be the same; she would never set foot inside it again, and all the gossips would have a wonderful time speculating about what her father had done with his fortune to leave his daughter penniless when he died.

In a way, it was that which hurt the worst. He had been such a proud old man—he would have absolutely hated to have his affairs chewed over in that way by all and sundry. For herself, it didn't much matter; she was quite used to being the subject of that sort of attention—one more topic would make little difference.

And she would manage well enough financially—after all, millions of other girls had to. There was bound to be *some* kind of job she could do. She would just have to get used to spending a great deal less on her clothes and other fol-de-rols, and not going to all those high society parties. Well, that suited her fine—she didn't much enjoy them anyway.

Oliver was watching her, a glint of faintly quizzical amusement in his dark eyes. 'Well...?' he hinted.

She drew in a long, deep breath; if he was going to behave like a normal buyer, she would behave like a normal vendor. But she wasn't going to make any effort to keep the sardonic edge from her voice. 'Well... As you can see, this is the hall,' she announced with a sweeping gesture of her hand. 'This is the oldest part of the house; it probably dates back to about the middle of the fifteenth century, though the panelling is rather later—probably from the reign of James the Second.'

'Hmm...' He nodded, glancing around with interest.

'Here on the left is the music room,' she went on, leading the way. 'The piano, like the rest of the furniture, is for sale with the house; it probably needs tuning—it hasn't been played for...quite a few years.' Since her mother died, in fact, but she didn't need to tell him that.

He came to join her in the doorway, crowding her, forcing her into retreat again. 'This is a nice room,' he commented with approval.

'Yes, it is.' Her favourite, when she had been little. In the afternoon the sun shone into it, gleaming on the dark polished walnut of the piano while her mother had played. And in the winter, a fire had always been kept burning in the fireplace. Unaware of the wistful sigh that slipped from her lips, she turned back to the hall.

'This is the dining room,' she announced, flinging open a wide pair of double doors. 'The table opens out to seat up to twenty people, but it is a bit of a squash with that many.'

'I know.'

Yes—dinner, the night of their engagement party. Seated together, side by side, him smiling down at her as they accidentally nudged elbows, as Alina watched silently, malevolently, from the other end of the table. Fiercely she pushed the memory away, slanting him a look of sharp annoyance. Either they were playing their roles or they weren't—he couldn't have it both ways.

'The mantelpiece is in the style of Adam,' she continued in a somewhat over-cooked pastiche of a tour guide. 'But I'm afraid it isn't the real thing. The mirror above it is rather fine, though. French, eighteenth century—you'll find the details in the inventory. Would you like to see the drawing room next?'

'Whatever you suggest,' he concurred. His smile left her in no doubt that he found her performance amusing. But then he could afford to laugh—he held the winning hand.

She turned abruptly on her heel, and stalked back into the hall. 'This is the newer wing of the house.' She marched briskly around the dog-leg at the back of the hall. 'Victorian. Fortunately, unlike a lot of Victorian buildings, it was built to blend in with the older part, rather than tacked on like some hideous brick carbuncle. In fact from the outside, with the ivy growing over it, it's really quite hard to tell the difference. It's only the different style of chimneys that give it away.'

'Is that so?'

She flashed him a look of icy disdain. He was deliberately trying to needle her, but she was determined not to let herself respond. 'The ceiling is considered to be a particularly fine example of Victorian plasterwork,' she persisted doggedly. 'The fireplace is Carrera marble, imported from Italy.'

'Very nice.' He strolled across the room to the open French windows that led out onto the terrace and the garden. 'I've always liked this garden,' he mused, stepping outside. 'You can wander in it for hours, and still keep finding something unexpected around another corner.'

Ginny's heart gave a sharp thud—seeing him standing

there on the terrace brought back a sudden vivid memory of that night when she had found him out here, almost in this very spot, with Alina in his arms. 'Nothing will ever change between us...' Words that could so easily be interpreted either way, according to what the listener had been primed to expect. A stepbrother reassuring a stepsister he was fond of, or a devious lover's vow?

And now...he had made it clear that he intended her to marry him. Buying the house—that was another part of the trap. If she married him, she could stay here—she wouldn't have to leave. No one would even have to know that she had had to sell it. If she married him...

He turned, those dark eyes seeming able to read her thoughts. 'So, are you going to show me the rest of the house?'

She stepped back sharply as he followed her into the hall, much too aware of him, much too vulnerable to that aura of raw masculinity he conveyed. He was casually dressed today, in cream-coloured chinos and a cool linen shirt, the sleeves folded back over his strong, sun-bronzed forearms, the collar unfastened to show that smattering of dark male hair at the base of his throat...

She drew in a ragged breath, struggling to fight the sudden surge of heat inside her. He was much too perceptive to miss the signals her treacherous body was giving out, and she had no doubt that he would be unscrupulous in taking advantage of any chink in her armour. With what she hoped was a smile of cool composure, she turned back towards the hall.

'That door leads to the kitchen...'

There was a resounding crash as she caught her knee against the umbrella stand, sending it crashing to the floor, umbrellas and walking sticks skittering across the hall.

Her cheeks flamed scarlet. Dammit—how could she

have been so clumsy? Quickly she stooped to gather them up, averting her head to hide her confusion—but as she reached for a brass-tipped ebony cane that her father had used Oliver bent to help her. Their hands brushed, fleetingly—and her breath seemed to stop in her throat as a sizzling charge of electricity tingled along her taut-strung nerve-fibres.

Somehow she didn't seem able to move, watching Oliver as he carefully set the stand upright again, gathering all the contents and putting them back into place. And then he turned back to her, offering her his hand to help her to her feet.

Her heart was beating so fast she was sure he must be able to hear it. Reluctantly she put her hand into his, though there was no way she was going to risk lifting her eyes to that dark, dangerous gaze. So much for her pose of cool self-assurance, she mused bitterly, if one touch of his hand could reduce her to a quivering jelly. She had to get a grip…!

'Shall we continue the tour?' he suggested blandly.

'Oh… Yes…' With an effort of will she managed to steady her voice. 'The only other room on this floor is my father's den—you don't need to see that. I'll show you upstairs.'

'Thank you.'

She was acutely aware of him following her as she walked up the stairs, could sense that insolently approving gaze watching the swaying of her neat derrière in the slim-cut grey silk trousers she had chosen to wear with a simple cashmere wrap-around top, to look smart but comfortable for the buyer she had been expecting. Damn him! She would almost rather the place was sold to a health club than that he should have it.

'There are five bedrooms on this floor, and two more on the floor above,' she recited flatly. 'Two of the bedrooms have their own bathrooms, and there's another one on this floor and one upstairs.'

'That seems adequate,' he drawled, baiting her with his lazy smile. 'Though at least at the beginning I shall only require one bed—so long as it's deep and comfortable. And wide enough for two.'

Her eyes flashed him a frost warning. Abandoning her pre-prepared script, she marched along the passage to open one door after another, leaving him to stroll along behind her, casually glancing into some of the rooms. How could she ever have thought she was in love with such an arrogant, insufferable man? Even at nineteen, she would have thought she'd have had more sense.

Most of the rooms hadn't been used for years, and she had spent the past couple of days airing them with the windows open, dusting them and shifting some of the furniture around to cover the threadbare patches on the carpets.

Oliver paused by the one door she hadn't opened. 'What's in here?' he queried, indicating it with a movement of his head.

She hesitated, her hands clenching as she held them behind her back. 'That's...my room,' she responded tautly.

He arched one dark, mocking eyebrow. 'So open it,' he insisted.

'You don't need to see my room,' she protested, her voice taut.

'I'm buying the whole house.'

It was silly really—if he had been an ordinary buyer she would have thought nothing of opening the door. But with him it seemed...almost like a physical violation. But he had the upper hand here; reluctant as she was, she really had little option but to accept his very good offer for the house—it was that or allow her father's estate to be declared bankrupt.

She opened the door.

The room had been decorated only last year; her conscience ached now when she thought about the expense, when her father had been concealing from her his desperate financial straits. In delicate shades of peaches and cream, with swathes of lace at the window and festooning the Queen Anne tester bed, it was pretty and feminine, without being too frou-frou.

With luck he wouldn't insist on seeing the dressing room; she was all too guiltily aware that it was stuffed full of all the dresses she didn't have room for at her flat—some of them hardly worn. At least it was fairly tidy in here—she had cast her eye over it an hour ago, while she was waiting...

Oh, *no!* How could she not have noticed that pair of dainty white silk French knickers, there on the floor? She must have dropped them when she was putting the laundry away. Her cheeks flushed a betraying shade of scarlet as she tried to move casually across the room to kick them discreetly under the bed, but he was ahead of her.

He picked them up, dangling them from his fingers to examine the exquisite lace edging, his eyes glinting with amused speculation. 'Very nice,' he accorded. 'You have expensive tastes in underwear.'

'Thank you,' she grated, snatching them and screwing them up in her hand, stuffing them into the nearest drawer of the dressing table.

'I like a woman to wear sexy underwear. It shows that she appreciates her own body.' His voice was huskily soft, his smile lazily mocking her. 'And that she knows how to please a man.'

She turned sharply away from him, walking over to look out of the window. Her cheeks were flaming hot, her mind spinning with images that she didn't know how to control. If he could do this to her with just a few words, a knowing smile...

A starling had alighted on the lawn and was tugging at a worm. She would miss the garden. The swing she'd used to play on when she was a little girl had long since gone, but the old oak tree was still there. It was odd that she hadn't noticed when her father had let go his gardener, and just employed a man to come in once a week to mow and tidy up.

The evidence of neglect was all too plain to see, now that she knew to look—hawksbeard growing up among the roses, a tangled mass of creeper scrambling all over the pergola, and the apple trees in the orchard beyond the old stone wall were sorely in need of some attention. Maybe at least Oliver would take care of them, instead of chopping them down...

He had come up very close behind her—so close that she could feel the warmth of his body, though he wasn't touching her. A small knot of tension was tautening in the pit of her stomach; there was no way she could disguise the effect he had on her. And she knew that he was quite ruthlessly exploiting that knowledge to close one gate of the trap. The other was the money.

'So—how's your little plan working out?' he enquired, his soft, sardonic voice taunting her.

'My...plan?'

'To hook yourself a wealthy husband. Any luck yet?'

She shrugged her slender shoulders, affecting an air of cool disdain.

He bent his head until his warm breath was stirring the soft tendrils of hair at the nape of her neck, where she had coiled it up loosely on the back of her head. 'Marry me, and I'll keep you in all the silk underwear you could ever want,' he murmured, velvet-soft, tempting her with an implicit promise far more beguiling than endless supplies of French lingerie.

It was a struggle to control her ragged breathing, and she was all too aware that looking down over her shoulder he had an excellent view of the agitated rise and fall of her breasts, firm and ripe beneath the fine-denier cashmere top. It was as if she had caught some kind of dangerous tropical fever that was heating her blood, making her dizzy.

'My sweet little Virginia, virginal and innocent.' He laughed in harsh mockery. 'Unfortunately I had that wrong, didn't I? When did you lose that precious innocence, I wonder? Not to Mark Ransome, surely?'

'Of course not!' Desperate to escape the spell he was spinning around her, she sidestepped quickly away from him, her own laughter brittle. 'It was *long* before that.'

'Oh?' One dark eyebrow arched in sardonic question. 'Who was the lucky man, then?'

'The first?' As her numbed brain sought rapidly for a name he couldn't associate with anyone he knew, her eyes fell on the rosewood writing desk beneath the window—French, eighteenth-century. 'Louis... His name was Louis.'

'Louis? He was French?'

'That's right. He was an exchange student who was staying with one of my schoolfriends. He had blue eyes.' It was remarkable how fluently the lies tripped from her tongue once she had begun. 'Blue eyes and blond hair. And a *gorgeous* body.'

The glint in his eyes conveyed an unmistakable hint of danger, but it was far too late for her to heed the warning. 'And after that?' he queried.

She shrugged, favouring him with a disdainful smile as she turned away from him. 'Oh heavens, Oliver,' she drawled languidly, 'you surely don't expect me to remember all of them?'

'I suppose not. It's ironic, really—there I was in New York, struggling to control my baser urges, trying to treat you gently, not to alarm you, and all the time you were probably wondering why I didn't just drag you straight off to bed. Perhaps I should make up for lost time now.'

She was halfway to the door when he caught her, snatching her wrist and spinning her back into his arms, laughing as she struggled in vain to be free. 'I let you run away from me once before,' he growled as his mouth came down to claim hers. 'You're not going to escape this time.'

She jerked her head back, but he twisted his fingers into the loose coil of her hair, letting the pins that held it fall to the floor as it unravelled, and he wound it around his hand, ruthlessly holding her prisoner. Her body was curved hard against his, her tender breasts crushed by the granite wall of his chest, but her eyes still spat angry defiance.

'I won't marry you,' she breathed. 'You can't make me.'

'Can't I?' His slow smile conveyed the satisfaction of certain victory. 'We'll see.'

She had been prepared to fight him, but how could she defend herself against the way he kissed her now? First his tongue, slow and languorous, tracing the full curve of her lips, teasing at the corners, coaxing them apart. And then his teeth, nibbling playfully but warning her that if necessary they could inflict a cruel punishment. He was letting her know that he was going to demand nothing less than her total surrender—and he had all the expertise to undermine her will to resist him.

She closed her eyes as a floating euphoria seeped

through her. His lips were moving over hers, hot and enticing, and on a low moan of submission she finally let them part, allowing his plundering tongue to invade deep into every sweet, secret corner of her mouth. His hand was roving deliciously down her spine, curving her even more intimately close against him, making her devastatingly aware of the raw tension of arousal in him.

It was difficult to breathe, impossible to think. She was aware only of that roving hand, stroking back up over her body now with unmistakable intent. A small gasp escaped her lips as she felt his strong fingers brush against the soft, full curve of her breast, and then mould around it, caressing it as the tender bud of her nipple hardened into his palm.

Heat flared inside her as he tilted her head to graze a path of scalding kisses down the length of her throat and into the sensitive hollow at its base, and it was only when they trailed on, along the line of her collarbone and over her bare shoulder, that she realised he had unfastened the wrap of her cashmere top and pushed it back, starting to undress her.

But her gasp of protest caught in her throat as his hand returned to her breast again, warm and firm through the delicate lacy cup of her bra. 'This is a pretty little scrap,' he remarked, finding the tiny hook that fastened it. 'I bet it cost a small fortune.'

Her eyes flew open in angry indignation, all the reasons why she shouldn't be allowing this to happen flooding back to shame her. But he had no difficulty in restraining her as she tried to push him away, and cashmere and lace were tossed casually to the floor as he caught both her wrists, tipping her backwards onto the bed and landing on top of her, pinioning her beneath his weight, both her hands pinned back above her head.

'So...' He laughed in husky satisfaction, holding her

down as he lifted himself to let his gaze wander down over the creamy ripe curves of her naked breasts, rosy tips prettily inviting. 'Very nice,' he accorded mockingly. 'Worth the wait.'

He had transferred both her wrists into the grip of one iron hand, to free the other, and she glared up at him in hot defiance, her jaw clenching as she determined to resist any pleasure from his caresses. But the glint of amusement in his dark eyes warned her that he had taken that as a challenge, and she had to bite her lip as his first light, tantalising touch stroked over her body.

His fingertips traced a lazy, meandering path, savouring every changing texture of her heated skin, circling over the aching ripeness of her breasts, tormenting her with a lingering anticipation that she feared would drive her out of her mind. His lazy smile taunted her, knowing that she was losing the battle of wills—and she no longer cared. She wanted him to strip her naked, take his pleasure of her body, subdue her with his hard male possession...

A hot spark of electricity shafted through her as at last he let his thumb brush lightly over the taut, waiting bud of her nipple, and she gasped in shock, her whole body melting into a pool of sensation as he teased the tender peak with tiny pinches, catching it between his fingers and rolling it beneath his flattened palm.

He no longer had to hold her prisoner by her wrists— she was lost in the erotic spell he had cast around her, her spine arching in feline grace to offer her body to more of those magical caresses. And as his dark head bent slowly over her breast she watched, scarcely breathing, some part of her dimly aware that her whole life had been on hold for the past six years and more, waiting for this.

His sensuous tongue rasped over the raw, tender peak

of her nipple, then swirled languorously around it, lapping at it and teasing it, flicking delicately as if it was a moist, succulent berry waiting for him to taste. A soft moan escaped her lips, and she writhed on the bed in delicious agony, her whole body aching with sweet sensations.

He lifted his head, his dark eyes wicked as sin as he moved to the other breast, treating it to the same expert torment, his hard white teeth nipping delicately at the tender bud, making it sizzle with raw sensitivity. And then, drawing it deep into his mouth, he began to suckle at it with a hungry rhythm that pulsed through her veins like fire.

'Is this what you want?' he taunted, his voice a husky rasp like velvet over stone. 'Do you want me to make love to you like this?' His hand had slipped down to stroke over her slender thighs. 'Do you want me to take you right now? Do you want to feel me inside you, thick and hard, *deep* inside you, making love to you until you can't even stand up?'

'Yes...' She had to drag for breath, pleading in a ragged desperation. 'Please, yes... Now...'

His laughter was a cruel whiplash of contempt. 'No—not now. On our wedding night.' He rose easily to his feet, his mocking gaze surveying her as she lay sprawled half-naked on the bed. 'Just think how the waiting will heighten the pleasure.'

Her eyes flew open and she stared up at him in shock. 'You...can't be serious!' she protested, bewildered.

'Never more so in my life,' he responded, his voice laced with sardonic humour. 'I can't be absolutely sure that some idiot like Jeremy won't be fool enough to marry you and let you spend all his money on frippery like this.' He bent and picked up the lacy scrap of her bra, casually tossing it to land on the rumpled coverlet beside her. 'But I'm quite certain that he could never give you what you need in bed. And I can. So if you want it, the choice is yours.'

She grabbed at her bra, clutching it in front of her as she somewhat belatedly covered her naked breasts with her arms. 'You must be crazy!' she gasped weakly. 'Why are you so set on marrying me?'

'I told you.' His dark eyes glinted dangerously. 'I wouldn't want anyone thinking you'd prefer to marry a pathetic fool like Jeremy, or any others of his ilk. You promised to marry me—very publicly. It's time to keep your promise.'

'You're the fool!' she threw at him a little desperately. 'I'd only be marrying you for your money. I'd make your life a misery.'

'You think so?' One dark eyebrow arched in quizzical amusement. 'Haven't you ever heard the saying that a woman who marries for money spends the rest of her life earning it? And I intend to see that you earn every penny—on your back. I think that could prove quite pleasurable.'

'I won't!' she insisted, forcing back the tears that were threatening to choke her voice. 'I won't marry you.'

He glanced at his watch, almost bored by the conversation. 'I'm afraid I have to be getting back to London,' he remarked, his tone as bland as if they had been discussing the weather. 'I shall be leaving for Tokyo this evening—I'll be away for a couple of weeks, but I'll be back in time for Howard's retirement party. I suggest you continue to liaise with his secretary over that. And when I get back, I shall expect your answer.'

She was still staring at him in stunned bemusement as he walked out of the room, closing the door quietly behind him.

CHAPTER SEVEN

THE retirement party was going very well. Discussing it with Uncle Howard's secretary, Ginny had realised that he had been at the bank for fifty years, so they had decided that a golden theme would be nice. Ginny had arranged to have the elegant oak-panelled boardroom decked out with masses of gold-coloured flowers—lilies and irises and huge frilly yellow chrysanthemums—and the food, too, picked up the colour scheme, with saffron sauces and garnishes of golden mango and star-fruit.

The centrepiece had been a large cake decorated with fine edible gold-leaf, to look like a golden sovereign, with Howard's rather distinctive profile in the centre, and his name and the dates of his chairmanship written around the edge. Everyone had been fascinated by it—and when it had been cut, after the speeches, they had declared that it tasted as good as it looked. Only the caterers knew that it hadn't come from them. It was Ginny's secret—her own personal contribution, over and above what Oliver had paid for.

Oliver. Her eyes slanted automatically across the room to where he stood with his father and the chairman of Preston Chemicals, one of their biggest clients. She hadn't seen him for almost three weeks—he had only arrived back from his trip to the Far East in the early hours of this morning. Any normal human being would have looked drained and jet lagged, she reflected tartly, but not him—he still looked fit enough to run a half-marathon and be back at his desk in time to make another few hundred thousand before the Stock Exchange closed.

The sale of the house, meanwhile, was proceeding in-exorably—contracts had already been exchanged. In just a few more weeks she would have to move out the last of her own things—those that weren't on the inventory that went with the estate—and say her goodbyes. She had tried hard not to think about it, except when she was forced to sign papers or agree other arrangements, but now that Oliver was back she had no doubt that he would push for even quicker progress.

As if he sensed her watching him, he glanced up, those dark eyes capturing hers from across the crowded room. They had exchanged only a few brief words since the beginning of the party—there had been no time for anything more...personal. But he had warned her that he was going to expect her answer today—and the glint in his eyes as they met hers across the room, the faintly sardonic quirk at the corner of his hard mouth, gave her no reason to hope for any respite.

With an effort of will, she managed to drag her gaze from his, turning him an aloof shoulder and looking around quickly for someone—anyone—to talk to, to keep her mind distracted from the confrontation she knew was to come. Her cousin Peter was conveniently close at hand, and he looked a little startled as she greeted him with a warm smile.

'Hello, Peter! How nice to see you.'

'You saw me on Sunday,' he responded, frowning slightly. 'You came to lunch.'

Ginny laughed a little too brightly, intent on showing anyone who cared to be watching that she was com-pletely relaxed, enjoying herself, not in the least bit wor-ried about anything. 'So I did! It's been such a busy week, the time seems to have rushed by.'

'Busy? You?' Her cousin's response was laced with irony. 'Don't tell me you had to get your nails done as *well* as going to the hairdressers!'

She shrugged her slender shoulders in a gesture of airy dismissal. 'Don't mock,' she retorted. 'I'll have you know that it's extremely hard work looking fashionable these days. Anyway, I went for a job interview as well.'

'Ah, yes—I remember you mentioned it on Sunday. Some PR firm, wasn't it? How did it go?'

'Er...quite well.' She would have loved to be able to wipe that cynical expression off his face by telling him that she was about to embark on an exciting new career in public relations. 'At least, the interview went well—they actually offered me the job. It was just...then they started telling me about one of the clients I'd be representing, and...well, it was a tobacco company.'

'So...?'

'But I couldn't work for a tobacco company,' she asserted, shocked.

'Why not?'

'Because...' Why had she even expected him to understand her scruples? It wasn't that Peter was unethical—he just believed that business was business. 'They sell cigarettes.' There was little point getting into an argument with him about it.

'Well, yes,' he concurred, as if talking to the village idiot. 'That's what tobacco firms do, usually—they sell cigarettes.'

'Don't try to tax poor Ginny's brain with such complicated details,' a sardonic voice remarked behind her. 'It's difficult enough for her to decide which lipstick to wear to go with her outfit.'

'Not at all.' She flashed Oliver an icy smile. 'With old gold, it could only be Brunique.'

'And you wear it so well,' he approved, letting his

gaze drift lazily down over the stylishly cut suit of slub-satin she had chosen to tone with the colour scheme of the party. Until this moment it had seemed perfectly respectable, but suddenly she felt herself wishing she had worn a blouse beneath the trim jacket, or had had the skirt left a little longer. His eyes returned to her soft mouth, and she felt a betraying blush of pink creep into her cheeks. 'Excuse us,' he added smoothly to Peter, taking her elbow with one deceptively light hand. 'I need to have a few words with Ginny. To thank her for all her hard work in arranging the party.'

'Of course...'

She knew there was no point in resisting as he deftly steered her away—that grip could tighten like a vice if he should so choose. And it would only create a quite unnecessary scene. So she held her head very erect, letting him lead her into a quiet alcove in one corner of the wood-panelled room.

'So...' He leaned one hand against the wall. 'You've done very well. It's an excellent party—my father is delighted.'

'Thank you,' she responded with frosty dignity. 'At least you have to admit that I'm capable of doing a *little* more than choose a lipstick.' She was still stinging from that mocking remark—did he really believe she was so stupid...? The next moment she was forced to concede that she probably was, as two wood-panelled doors slid silently shut and she realised that what she had thought was simply an alcove was in fact a lift. 'Where are we going?' she demanded, startled.

'Upstairs,' he responded, smiling like a jungle cat on his cornered prey.

'But...I don't want to go upstairs,' she protested, furious with herself for stepping so easily into his trap.

'We're there.' The lift doors slid smoothly open again,

and she found herself looking out at a large, high-
ceilinged room of similar dimensions to the boardroom
on the floor below. But this one was littered with decora-
tors' debris—planks and stepladders propped against the
walls, the floor and furniture covered with paint-
spattered tarpaulins.

'I...want to go back downstairs,' she insisted a little
unsteadily. 'I... People will wonder where we are.'

'I doubt if anyone will even notice we've gone,' he
responded laconically. 'Howard's the centre of attention
this afternoon. Surely you're not afraid to be alone with
me for a few minutes?'

'Of course not...'

'Good. Then let's have a drink.'

She hesitated, struggling not to let him see the tension
that was knotting inside her. The moment had come
when she was going to have to tell him her decision—
she wasn't going to marry him. All she had to do was
tell him that, and then leave. After all, what could he do
to her?

He could throw her out of her family home.

Yes, well... She'd survive. She had her apartment,
even though the annual lease had almost expired, and
she couldn't afford to renew it.

He could taint her father's memory with the humilia-
tion of bankruptcy.

But then her father wasn't here to be hurt by it. And
even if he made life difficult for her—which he had already demonstrated himself perfectly capable of doing—
she would fight him. Okay, so her first foray into the job
market hadn't proved very successful, but there were
other jobs. And she really wouldn't be sorry to leave her
present life behind—she would only be sorry that she
would no longer be able to raise so much money for the
charities she had helped in the past.

'Martini?' Oliver enquired, strolling across to a small but well-appointed kitchen that was separated from the main room by a latticed screen.

'Th-Thank you.' This was silly. All she had to do was step back into the lift and press the button to take it back down to the party below. But a swift check told her that the button, or whatever operated it, was cleverly concealed in the panelling, and she didn't want to have to instigate an undignified search for it.

As soon as she stepped out into the room the lift doors slid shut behind her—and another startled glance over her shoulder confirmed that the button on this floor was also concealed. She managed some kind of brittle laugh. 'Clever,' she accorded, a trace of acid on her tongue. 'Like having a priest's hole.'

'It's a little more convenient than running up and down the stairs,' he responded blandly, returning with the drinks and handing her a glass. 'Please excuse the state of the place—as you can see, I'm having it decorated. It hadn't been used for some time—my grandfather originally had it converted for use as a *pied-à-terre* in the City during the war, when travelling was difficult. I thought it might serve the same purpose again, though the problem is now traffic congestion rather than the blitz.'

'A good idea,' she conceded, sipping sparingly at her drink as she glanced around. A sample of wallpaper was taped to the wall—maroon and navy stripes; uncompromisingly masculine, like the man whose lair this would be. To her left was a French window which opened out onto a small roof garden, and, glad to find an excuse to put some space between them, she went out to look.

A small paved area, big enough for a green-painted cast-iron table and some chairs and a few tubs of flowers, was framed in green trellis, thickly tangled with honeysuckle and clematis, which shaded it from the sun and shielded it from the windows of the taller blocks of the City all around it. And by some lucky quirk the buildings opposite seemed to open out, giving a view all the way to the river, silver-grey in the afternoon sunshine. It was a tiny corner of paradise, hidden high above the roofs of the City.

'Like it?' he enquired, strolling out behind her.

'It's...very nice,' she managed, wishing her heart wouldn't race like that whenever he came near her.

'I thought about having this glassed in, but actually I quite like it as it is.'

'Oh, yes. You get a lovely breeze here from the river. And, with it facing south, it could get far too hot under glass...' She knew she was babbling, but she couldn't seem to stop herself.

'That's what I thought.' His smile warned her that he was perfectly well aware of the effect he was having on her. 'Come and tell me which of these carpet samples you like.'

Maybe it was just the sun that was heating her blood. But when she followed him back into the cooler shadows of the room, she knew she couldn't blame that. He had laid out several samples of carpet on the tarpaulin-covered table—variations on the maroon and navy theme—and somehow she managed to direct her feet to carry her over in that direction, managed to survey the options with some degree of composure.

'I think...I prefer that one,' she decided, choosing one almost at random.

'Hmm. I'm not sure. I think I like this one best,' he mused, selecting a different one.

She shrugged, taking a gulp of her drink to try to quell the dryness of her mouth. 'Whichever. Why are you asking me, anyway?'

'I thought that once we're married you might as well give up your apartment, and we can both use this when we want to stay in town.'

She drew in a ragged breath, conscious that the shaking of her hand was betrayed by the clinking of the ice in her glass. 'I...haven't said I'll marry you,' she protested tautly, not quite able to lift her eyes to meet his, focusing instead on the knot of his tie.

'No, you haven't.' His voice was very even, but she could sense the underlying hint of warning.

Somehow she managed to tilt up her chin, her gaze defiant. 'I really don't think you're the sort of husband I want,' she asserted with dignity.

He laughed without humour. 'I thought money was the only consideration?'

'Of course it isn't,' she retorted. 'I want to marry someone who...shares my interests, who has similar views on life.'

'You mean someone you can keep under your thumb.' He had perched casually on the edge of the table, his arms folded as he regarded her with cool amusement. 'A mistake, little Virginia. You need a husband who won't let you walk all over him. And you know I won't. Though don't let me stop you from trying,' he added, a glint of provocative humour in his eyes. 'I find it most entertaining.'

'So we'd do nothing but fight,' she concluded acidly. 'That doesn't sound like a very good basis for marriage.'

'Oh, don't worry.' His hard mouth quirked into a sardonic smile. 'I don't intend it to be.'

He reached out and took the lapels of her jacket, and before it had even occurred to her befuddled brain to resist he had drawn her towards him, trapping her against the table, pinning her there between his strong thighs. With a cool ruthlessness he began to unfasten the buttons, brushing the satin fabric aside to uncover the ripe, creamy swell of her breasts.

'*This* will be the basis of our marriage.' He let his dark gaze linger in mocking approval over the soft, feminine curves, straining with every ragged breath against the taut lacy cups of her bra. 'Sex.'

He growled the last word against her mouth as he claimed it with his, hot and demanding, stifling any word of protest she might have uttered. But she wasn't protesting. She had put up her hands against his chest in some last instinctive gesture of defence, but she had encountered the warm resilience of hard male muscle, and the need that had been aching inside her since the last time he had kissed her melted into a helpless surrender.

His hot tongue swirled deep into her mouth in a flagrantly erotic exploration, plundering every sweet, secret corner to ignite her responses. The heady scent of his skin was drugging her mind, silencing any last whispers of warning. He had curved her back against the table, and she hadn't even noticed when he had unfastened her bra, brushing the useless scraps of lace aside to caress her naked breasts with his strong, sensitive fingers, teasing the tender nipples until they hardened into exquisitely sensitised buds, red as roses.

It was like some kind of crazy sickness, a fever in her blood that made her want him so much that she didn't care about anything else. His kisses, his touch, were the only thing that could satisfy her craving, but, like an addict, every time she yielded to temptation it only left her needing him more.

Her hair had tumbled down from the neat coil she had twisted onto the back of her head, and he raked his fingers down through its silken length, a low growl of pleasure escaping his throat. 'Don't ever cut it,' he rasped insistently. 'Not one inch.'

Some defiant part of her mind resolved indignantly to have it all chopped off at the first opportunity. But she wouldn't. He liked it, and she needed every last weapon in her armoury to fuel the heat of his lust for her—until maybe one day what was now a purely physical desire could begin to grow into something stronger. It was the only hope she had to cling to.

His kisses were dusting a path of fire over her trembling eyelids, finding the pulse that raced beneath her temple, swirling into the dainty shell of her ear and then moving on, as he dragged on her hair to tilt her head back, exposing her throat in a vulnerable curve beneath his hot mouth. He knew just where to find the sensitive spot in the hollow of her shoulder, sending shivering sparks through her, making her gasp raggedly for breath.

And then his mouth moved on again, as he arched her across the table, her head tipped back and her eyes closed, her naked breasts with their taut rosebud peaks offered up invitingly to his exquisite caresses. He cupped the ripe, firm flesh in his hands, as if they were two succulent peaches, his tongue lapping and rasping over each pert nipple in turn, swirling around them, nipping lightly at them with his hard white teeth, suckling deeply at first one, then the other, reducing her to a state of mindless ecstasy.

His thighs were between hers, easing them apart, and he was moving against her with a slow, grinding rhythm—and unconsciously she was responding. The hem of her slim-cut skirt had ridden up to the tops of her silk stockings—and it was as she became aware of the brush of his fingers against her bare skin, lifting her skirt even higher, that she felt a sudden stab of panic.

'No...!' She struggled to drag in the breath to protest, her hands at last finding the will to push him away. 'Please... No.'

Dark eyes quizzed hers with sardonic humour. 'No?'

Scarlet shame flooded her cheeks as she realised what a wanton picture she must present, her hair tumbled around her shoulders, her make-up smudged, the rosy crests of her nipples still dewy-moist from his ravaging mouth. But, screwing up every ounce of will-power she possessed, she shook her head. 'You…said you were going to…wait until our wedding night,' she reminded him in ragged desperation.

'So I did.' His smile was hard, ruthless. 'But you haven't said yet that you're going to marry me.'

She had to drop her lashes, unable to hold that mocking gaze. Damn her traitorous heart—where no other reason was strong enough to force her, it left her no choice. 'Okay… Yes. I'll…marry you,' she whispered.

He put his hand beneath her chin, tilting up her head, forcing her to face him. 'Repeat that,' he ordered gruffly.

She hesitated, waiting until her breathing had steadied enough for her to say it coolly. 'I'll marry you. If you're not bothered that I'm only marrying you for the money, why should I have any scruples?'

'Oh, not only for the money,' he countered, those dark eyes glinting in sardonic amusement. 'This too.' In a gesture of calculated insolence he put his hand on her breast again, moulding its ripe shape in a gesture of arrogant possession. 'Your body responds so delightfully. The pleasures that await us will be entirely mutual.'

She brushed him away, turning him an aloof shoulder as she walked with as much dignity as she could manage to the other side of the room. 'Yes, well…I dare say,' she conceded minimally. Her fingers fumbled to refasten the catch of her bra, but the rasp of the lace against her rawly sensitised nipples was still a little too sharp, so instead she concentrated on coiling up her hair, pinning it in place with as many of the pins as she could find.

'I don't think there's any reason why we should pro-long our engagement,' Oliver remarked, watching her with the lazy satisfaction of a victor surveying his spoils. 'We'll announce it right away, and set the date for...shall we say four weeks?'

'Four *weeks?*' she repeated weakly. 'As soon as that?'

'Why not?'

She could think of no reply, so she shrugged her slim shoulders in an airy gesture of dismissal. 'If you like. It's not as if we're going to go over the top with a church wedding and all the trimmings.'

'Oh, but we are,' he countered. 'Every last detail. I'm quite sure most of our guests will be able to come, in spite of the short notice, and as for the other arrange-ments—I doubt if that will be a problem, given that money will be no object.'

She flashed him a look of frosty disdain—that was her only defence against him now. 'Very well. I'd better see about choosing a dress as soon as possible—it'll take several fittings, you know. And I'll speak to Edmund about the catering while he's finishing up this afternoon.'

'I shall leave all that in your capable hands.' He had strolled into the kitchen and washed his hands, and now he was wiping them on a paper towel. Ginny frowned.

'You've got paint on your hand.'

He glanced down at it in innocent unconcern. 'So I have.'

With a slow-dawning realisation she began to put two and two together, staring at him in cold fury before brushing aside the fabric of her jacket to look down at her own body. The imprint of his hand, clear and sharp, covered her left breast like a brand of possession. 'You...bastard!' she breathed.

He merely laughed, the humour biting. 'I'm afraid it's a special acrylic-based paint. It won't do you any harm, but now it's dry it won't come off for several weeks. Long enough to remind you, just in case you were thinking of playing around between now and our wedding, of just who you belong to.'

'I don't *belong* to you,' she threw back at him heatedly. 'I'm not an object—you don't own me.'

'Oh, but I do,' he countered, his voice very soft but laced with a distinct note of warning. 'I've bought you— just like I've bought your house. You can spend as much of my money as you please on your dresses and your jewellery, and whatever else you want to indulge yourself with, and in return I get exclusive rights over that very lovely body. That's the deal.'

'Take it or leave it?'

He shook his head. 'You've already said you're taking it. You don't back out on me twice.'

She tilted up her chin, glaring back at him defiantly. 'And if I do?'

That smile could freeze over hell. 'I wouldn't recommend it,' he responded. 'I'll send the lift up for you in ten minutes. That should give you enough time to make yourself…decent again.' And, stepping into the lift, he disappeared as the doors slid silently shut.

'Well, aren't you a dark horse? You never even told me, and I'm your best friend!'

Ginny managed some sort of crooked smile. She had only just stepped out of the lift when an indignant Sara accosted her—she had barely had a moment to catch her breath. 'I'm…sorry, Sara,' she responded a little unsteadily. 'It was…all a bit sudden.'

Sara smiled, hugging her with warm affection. 'Oh, love—I'm so happy for you! I always knew you two were perfect for each other. Didn't I always say so, Peter?'

'Ad nauseam,' her husband confirmed dryly. 'But I'm very happy for you, Gin. Just don't forget you're lucky to have a second chance—don't blow it this time.'

'Oliver's the lucky one!' Sara protested loyally, tucking her arm into Ginny's. 'Oliver said you're getting married next month…?'

'That's right.' He had certainly wasted no time, she reflected, slanting a fleeting glance across the room, to where he stood talking to his father.

Sara was almost bursting with excited curiosity. 'It's awfully quick…?' she hinted.

'I'm not pregnant, if that's what you're thinking,' Ginny assured her with a wry smile.

'Oh, *no*—of course I didn't think that!' Her friend blushed, too transparent to lie easily. 'Well, perhaps the thought *did* cross my mind—but only for a teeny-tiny moment…'

'Don't be silly,' declared Aunt Margot, coming to join them. 'Even if she was, that would be no reason to rush, not these days.' She leaned forward and kissed Ginny affectionately on the cheek. 'I just wanted to tell you how very pleased I am,' she went on warmly. 'It's the best thing that could possibly happen. And I think it's very sensible of Oliver to want to have it all settled and done while Alina's away.'

'She's…away?' Ginny queried, trying not to sound too startled.

'That's right. You didn't know? I assumed Oliver would have told you. She's in the clinic again—another breakdown, I'm afraid.' The older woman sighed sadly. 'I expect Oliver thinks it would be better if the wedding takes place while she's there, being looked after. She's occasionally been a little…silly about things in the past.'

'Has she…?'

Ginny's response was vague, as her mind spun with

this unexpected news. Though, now she came to reflect on it, perhaps it didn't really come as too much of a surprise to discover that Alina had a history of some kind of mental fragility. She had always half suspected it, though she had told herself that she wasn't really a very objective judge where Alina was concerned. It did surprise her a little that this was the first she had heard about it, but then it seemed to have been something the family had kept a closely guarded secret. Her father had probably known, but it wouldn't have been the sort of thing he would have talked about. And Oliver...

Oliver was walking towards her now, with his father, and her heart gave a sharp thud as all other thoughts slid from her brain. Howard kissed her, expressing his delight, and she murmured something appropriate in response.

'Might as well make the announcement now, eh, son?' he suggested. 'Doesn't seem much point in delaying things.'

'Why not?' Oliver agreed easily. He put his hand in his pocket and brought out a small, dark blue velvet jeweller's box that Ginny remembered with an acute stab of pain. The last time she had seen it she had been an innocent nineteen, naively in love. Now she was six years older—and still in love with him, dammit. But the innocence and naivety were gone—this time she wasn't deluding herself that he was in love with her.

'Ladies and gentlemen...' Howard had stepped into the middle of the room, raising his voice for attention. 'As a perfect ending to a perfect retirement party, I would like to make a personal announcement—one that gives me the very greatest pleasure. May I ask you to charge your glasses and raise a toast? To my son, and his new fiancée...' With a sweep of his hand, he directed everyone's eyes to where Oliver and Ginny stood. 'The happy couple.'

'Ginny?'

Oliver was smiling down at her, a smile perfect enough to fool anyone watching them—only she could see the glint of sardonic amusement in his dark eyes as he forced her to go through with the charade. Reluctantly she held out her left hand and let him slip the ring onto it—it was still a perfect fit. The green heart flashed fire as he lifted her hand to his lips, laying a light kiss on her fingertips.

'To Ginny and Oliver!' The toast rang around the room, followed by a ripple of applause. Ginny gazed up into Oliver's eyes, feeling as though she might drown in their dark, dangerous depths. What would all these nice people think, she wondered abstractedly, if they knew that beneath her chic old-gold suit the imprint of his hand was branded onto her naked breast, like some primitive totem of possession?

How had she let things turn out like this, when she had quite definitely made up her mind that she was going to tell him that she *wouldn't* marry him? She wouldn't have been able to stop herself loving him, any more than she would have been able to call down the moon, but she could have learned to live with it. But being married to him...

He had bought her to be his 'slave' for one day. But now his ring was back on her finger and the memory of his hot, possessive touch was seared onto her skin—and she knew, with a certainty that ached inside her like a fever, that he had made her his slave for life.

CHAPTER EIGHT

'YOU look as if you'd like to stab me with that knife, not cut the cake with it,' Oliver remarked, an inflection of sardonic humour in his voice.

'What an excellent idea,' Ginny murmured, keeping her smile fixed in place as the photographer adjusted his lens. 'It would solve all my problems in one stroke.'

He laughed in dry amusement. 'Oh, no—it would be such a pity to get blood all over that lovely dress. I must say, it's really quite stunning—no doubt it's cost me a small fortune?'

'Of course.'

'From this angle, the view is worth every penny,' he taunted, his voice taking on a husky timbre. Since he was standing just behind her shoulder, the view he was appreciating was of the soft valley between her breasts. The shawl neckline of tiered lace was actually quite modest, but she might have known that he would find a way to make her feel uncomfortable.

It was only a couple of days ago that she had finally been able to get the last faint traces of his hand-print off her skin. His mark of possession; for the past month every time she had looked at herself in the mirror she had seen it there, evoking all too vividly the memory of the way his hand had moulded and caressed her naked breast—and the memory, too, that he now claimed exclusive privileges that she would deny at her peril.

The past few weeks had been frenetic with all the preparations. Which was probably just as well, she mused wryly—it had given her no time for second thoughts. Even this morning she had been dashing about, answering a hundred and one last-minute queries from the caterers and making sure the flowers had arrived as the hairdresser fussed around her, while Sara had sat calmly amid the chaos stitching her long lace veil to her headdress.

And now, almost before she had had time to take in that it was really happening, it was done. The vows had been spoken, the register signed, the photographs duly taken to record the happy event. Somehow she had managed to keep a smile in place throughout—did she really look as if she was blissfully happy? Certainly no one seemed to have noticed anything amiss. Maybe every bride had to keep convulsively sipping her champagne because her mouth was as dry as a desert, and avoid lifting her eyes to meet her bridegroom's gaze.

'I must congratulate you on the arrangements,' Oliver went on quietly. 'You've managed everything with your usual panache.'

'Thank you.'

'You've exceeded my expectations.' That mocking note was there in his voice again. 'I wonder if you can continue to do so? I look forward to finding out—a little later.'

She drew in a sharp breath, conscious of the way it lifted her breasts against the delicate ivory lace of her dress. Later... They were flying to Paris for the first few days of their honeymoon, and then on to another unknown destination where, Oliver had assured her, they would be guaranteed absolute privacy for two whole weeks. He had told her not to bother packing very much...

'That's it—just one more smile, please...' At last the photographer had finished, and one of the smart young waiters supplied by the caterers came to take the cake away and cut it.

'Don't forget to save the top tier!' Aunt Margot reminded him excitedly. 'You have to keep that for the first christening!'

'Of course.' Oliver still had his arm around Ginny's waist, curving her against his side. 'I shall enjoy making you pregnant,' he murmured, leaning close to her so that only she could hear.

She stared up at him in shock, trying in vain to pull discreetly away from him. 'That wasn't...part of the deal,' she protested raggedly.

'Of course it was.' Those dark eyes glinted. 'Perhaps I'll keep you continually pregnant—that way there'll be no risk of you being tempted to run around being unfaithful to me with nerds like Jeremy.'

'I...wouldn't do that,' she countered, forcing herself to meet his gaze levelly.

'You certainly won't while I'm around,' he insisted, an unmistakable note of warning in his voice. 'Unfortunately I won't be able to be around all the time. And I wouldn't trust you as far as I can spit.'

'Well, that's mutual,' she returned in a low hiss. 'At least we both know what we're getting.'

'Don't we just.' His smile was for public consumption, but she wasn't deceived. Marriages, according to the romantic myth, were supposed to be made in heaven—but this one had definitely been made in hell!

The band was playing the sort of easy-dancing music that everyone could enjoy, from two of Oliver's small cousins in their pretty bridesmaids' dresses to his elderly great-aunt. Ginny was circling sedately around the flower-decked marquee on the back lawn with her new father-in-law, the cascading lace of her veil drifting around her bare shoulders, the train of her skirt caught up by a ribbon hoop around her wrist.

A few feet away from her Oliver was dancing dutifully with one of his aunts, and she was able to watch him covertly from beneath her lashes. She could still see why she had fallen in love with him when she was a teenager, she reflected, a small ache in her heart. At that time it had been enough to take an inventory: crisp dark hair, sculpted cheekbones, a strongly carved jaw. But it was the intriguing sensuality of that hard mouth, the excitingly dangerous glint in those dark eyes that had held her interest. And then there was the way he laughed, low and slightly husky, the way he had eaten ice creams with her in Battery Park...

And then there was the way he kissed, wrapping her up in those strong arms, his mouth warm and sure, his caresses so sensuous, so skilful... She wanted him so much it hurt. And now she was his wife. His wife... She let the words roll around in her brain, savouring them, letting herself linger just for a moment in the beguiling fantasy that being married to him would be everything she had once dreamed...

But as he turned, and caught her eye, the fantasy fled. Tonight, in Paris, she would begin to pay the price for the blow to his male pride of that fateful night six years ago.

Uncle Howard, unaware of these jumbled thoughts, smiled down at her kindly. 'You know, I'm so happy that you're really a part of our family at last,' he told her. 'And your father would have been very pleased to know that you will be safely looked after. You're inheriting a great deal of money—that sort of thing can attract...the wrong sort of suitor. But with Oliver you can be quite sure it's nothing of the sort.'

Ginny stared at him, puzzled. 'But…didn't you know?' she stammered. 'About what happened?'

'What happened?' he repeated blankly. 'I don't know what you mean.'

Ginny hesitated. 'I had assumed that Daddy would have talked to you.' Actually she hadn't assumed— Oliver had told her. 'I mean, I know you weren't his banker…'

'Oh, no.' Uncle Howard shook his head, smiling. 'We agreed on that a long time ago. Friendship and financial matters don't mix, so we made a pact never to discuss them. Your father held his account elsewhere, and he never asked for my advice and I never offered it. It's the best way. Even with the best will in the world, things can go wrong. In fact, if you don't mind me offering a suggestion, I think you would be wise to follow the same policy with Oliver. Keep your fortune completely separate, and have your own financial adviser to discuss your investments with. I'm sure he would agree that it's the best policy.'

'Yes…' Through the spin of confusion in her mind she had almost instinctively decided to say nothing. 'Yes, that's good advice,' she murmured. 'Thank you.'

So Oliver had lied—it couldn't have been his father who had told him about her father's financial crisis, because Uncle Howard hadn't known. So how *had* he found out? And why had he lied?

But there was little time to think about that now—she had other things on her mind. Sara and a couple of her other closest friends were standing by the entrance to the marquee on tiptoe, to peep over the heads of the other dancers and catch her eye, and Sara was pointing to her watch. It was time to go and get changed into her 'going away' outfit.

Uncle Howard chuckled fondly. 'Ah—I think you're

being summoned,' he declared. 'Off you go and get ready, my dear.' He pecked a kiss onto her cheek. 'I'll see you again to say goodbye before you leave for Paris.'

'Of course.'

As discreetly as she could she slipped away to join her friends, and, giggling together, they hurried up through the garden, where dusk was already gathering beneath the wisteria-covered pergola and shadowing the long grass beneath the old apple trees in the walled orchard. They crossed the terrace, where six years ago Ginny had overheard that fateful conversation and thrown her emerald engagement ring back in Oliver's face, and, slipping into the house through the French windows, climbed the stairs to Ginny's bedroom.

Not her bedroom any more—the bedroom she would share with Oliver. At the back of the house, with three tall windows that overlooked the garden, it was of gracious proportions, the high ceiling coved and curlicued with plaster, the substantial marble fireplace providing an elegant focal point.

Money being no object, she had gone to town, with yards and yards of white satin and lace against walls of pale buttercup-yellow, and pale Chinese silk rugs on the polished parquet floor. The bed she had bought at an antiques auction, bidding outrageously—by Hepplewhite, it had fluted mahogany posts and a delicate pattern of leaves and flowers carved onto the tester. And she had had two French chaise longues from one of the other rooms re-upholstered—at enormous expense—to stand on each side of the fireplace.

There were two dressing rooms—one for Oliver and one for herself. Hers was still littered with the debris of getting ready for the ceremony—tissue paper, wrappings, several damp towels—and she glanced around wryly. 'What a mess! It looks as if a herd of elephants has been on the rampage in here.'

Sara gurgled with laughter. 'Oh, never mind—leave it now. You've got much more important things to think about.'

Ginny concealed a wry smile. Even though Sara was her best friend, she hadn't been able to bring herself to confide in her—maybe she was too steeped in the habit of pretending that everything was fine to be able to express her secret worries. Peter, a little more perspicacious, had perhaps guessed that something wasn't quite right, but he had asked no questions.

'Didn't the little bridesmaids look absolutely *scrumptious?*' Sara declared. 'And they were so well behaved. Do you remember at Cassy Clayton's wedding, when one of her little nieces decided that her sister's posy was nicer than her own and started to fight over it? I thought it was *so* funny! I know I shouldn't have laughed, but I just couldn't help it.'

'I remember,' Ginny chuckled, glad of the diversion to keep her mind off the evening ahead. 'And her sister got her own back later by smearing jam all down the back of her dress. And Cassy's grandfather told Maddy Ratcliffe's sister-in-law that she danced like a hippopotamus, and as she went to walk away she fell over one of the flower tubs and ended up sitting there on the ground, surrounded by roses and carnations, with her hat over her nose.'

'Oh, that was cruel!' protested gentle Sara, though she couldn't help but join in the laughter. 'Here, Ginny, do you want to take your dress off first, or shall I help you with your veil?'

'Let me get out of this dress,' Ginny responded. 'Then I can sit down more easily while you do the veil. Can you just reach the zip for me...?'

The door swung slowly open; Ginny had her back to it, but she was facing the mirror, and as she glanced up, startled, she saw Oliver, one wide shoulder resting lazily against the doorframe, his dark eyes glinting with sardonic amusement. She stilled, her heartbeat pounding, staring at the unexpected apparition as if staring at the devil himself.

'Oliver!' Sara giggled. 'You're not supposed to come in here.'

He quirked one quizzical eyebrow, his smile teasing. 'Why not?'

'Ginny's getting changed into her going away outfit.'

'So I see.' His voice took on a deliberately husky timbre, hinting at wicked intentions. 'I thought I might...be of some assistance.'

'Oh...!' Sara giggled in delight, pretending to be shocked. She glanced at the other girls. 'I think we'd better go back to the party,' she whispered excitedly. 'Come on.'

For a fleeting moment Ginny was tempted to beg them not to desert her, but they would certainly think she was completely crazy. She still stood with her back to the door, watching Oliver in the mirror, one hand holding up her dress, her mouth dry. Somehow she managed a vague smile for her friends as they skipped, laughing, from the room—if any of them *had* noticed anything amiss, hopefully they would simply assume that she was suffering from a last-minute dose of wedding nerves.

Oliver let the door swing shut behind them, his eyes still holding Ginny's through the mirror's reflection. Very slowly she turned to face him.

That hard mouth had quirked into a smile of arrogant satisfaction—the victor savouring his spoils. 'I believe you were taking off the dress,' he taunted. 'Don't let me stop you.'

She drew in a long, slow, steadying breath, only a supreme effort of will enabling her to keep her head up, defiantly returning that sardonic gaze. But it was a little late for defiance now—she had taken her vows; there was nowhere to run. Lowering her gaze, she half turned away from him, her hands trembling slightly as she slipped out of the sumptuously beaded satin and lace, making a great issue of laying it out across a chair and folding up the train off the floor in a last effort to delay the inevitable moment.

'It's certainly quite a dress,' Oliver remarked, a note of lazy mockery in his voice. 'But don't you think white was a little...inappropriate?'

'Inappropriate?' she repeated, wilfully refusing to respond to his innuendo.

'I thought it was supposed to symbolise the unsullied virginity of the bride,' he taunted. 'Isn't yours a little...sullied?'

'No, it isn't,' she retorted, stung.

One dark eyebrow arched in mocking surprise. 'It isn't? Oh, come on—you don't expect me to believe that.'

'Why not?' She turned to confront him, wishing now that she hadn't let him goad her into blurting it out. 'It's the truth.'

He didn't answer her. There was an arrested look in those dark eyes, and suddenly she felt a shiver of heat scud down her spine. She was still wearing her veil, the cascade of white embroidered net like a waterfall down her back, but now, as she faced him, he was able to inspect for the first time the results of her foray into one of Bond Street's most luxurious lingerie boutiques.

The sheer white lace basque tightly encased her slender shape, cupping the creamy swell of her breasts to emphasise their ripe curves. And with every ragged breath she could feel the tender rosy peaks rasp against the delicious constraint, knowing that their pink pertness must be invitingly visible through the delicate fabric.

The lace skimmed down over the smooth plane of her stomach and curved high over her thighs, with suspenders to hold up her white silk stockings. The kitten heels of her white satin bridal slippers enhanced the coltish length of her legs, and her only jewellery, apart from the engagement and wedding rings on her finger, was her grandmother's pearl choker, five elegant strands encircling her throat.

Oliver was taking his time, letting his dark gaze slide slowly down over her, lingering in insolent appreciation over every inch. 'Very nice,' he approved smokily. 'It's always more fun to unwrap a parcel when it's so attractively packaged.'

Her eyes flashed in cold indignation, but she didn't trust herself to speak.

Without taking his eyes from her, he put up his hand and loosened his tie, dropping it onto the chair beside him, and then shrugged out of his jacket with a movement of those powerful shoulders that made her mouth go suddenly dry. 'You'd better take that veil thing off,' he suggested. 'It's likely to cause one of us an injury.'

Her fingers felt numb, and she was all too acutely aware that as she lifted her hands to untangle the circlet from her hair her breasts lifted too, taut beneath the encasing lace cups of her basque. He didn't miss the movement, a flame igniting in his dark eyes as he watched her, his sensuous mouth smiling in mocking anticipation.

It took her several uncomfortable moments to get the thing off, hating him for making her provide him with such an erotic display. She almost threw it onto the chair as her hair tumbled down around her shoulders in a gleaming dark wave, and then turned to confront him again, her hands on her hips, her eyes glaring.

He seemed amused by her defiance. 'So tell me,' he queried, 'if you're supposed to be a virgin, where does Louis fit in?'

'Louis?' she repeated blankly.

'The handsome young French student who was supposed to have been your first lover.'

'Oh...' She felt a hot blush of pink rise to her cheeks. 'He didn't exist. I...made him up.'

'And the others?'

'There weren't any others.' She tilted up her chin, struggling to keep her voice steady. 'It was...just a load of cheap gossip.'

'They were lying?' He arched one dark eyebrow in cynical question. '*All* of them?'

'All of them,' she confessed, feeling as though he was stripping away every layer of defence she had.

'Explain.'

She shrugged her slender shoulders. He would know if she was lying, but she didn't want to tell him the whole truth. 'I suppose...they all just... It began with Mark. Nothing happened with him...' Her soft mouth twisted into a wry grimace. 'Apart from anything else he was much too drunk. But after that all the boys I went out with assumed that I *would*. And I didn't like that, so...I wouldn't. But of course none of them wanted to admit to his mates that they hadn't got anywhere—I suppose they were afraid they'd be laughed at.' There was a bitter note in her voice. 'So...they made things up—and as each story was added on to the rest everyone believed them. There was nothing I could do about it— no one would have believed me anyway.'

'Well, well...!' His laughter was soft and husky. 'You really have exceeded my expectations.' He moved slowly towards her. 'Who would have thought it? A virgin bride.' He lifted his hand, stroking it up over her throat to tilt her face to his, his eyes like dark fires as they gazed down into hers. 'I've waited six years for this,' he growled. 'But now...the waiting stops.'

The kiss that he laid on her trembling lips was a tantalising promise, sweet and sensuous as his hot tongue traced a languorous path over the delicate membranes just within her mouth. But at the moment she began to melt in response he drew back, leaving her swaying on unsteady legs. Turning, he walked into the bedroom and stretched himself out on the bed, leaving her hesitating, uncertain.

'Come here,' he commanded, his voice soft but implacable.

She had to draw in a long, slow breath to steady the uncomfortable racing of her heartbeat. Was her pride worth the pain of not telling him that she loved him? But pride was the only thing she had—he had long ago enslaved her heart, and now he would enslave her body for his pleasure. She could only hope that in time the intimacy of the marriage bed would mellow his feelings towards her, that maybe one day he might begin to feel something more than the desire to punish her.

But for now...she could only obey the compelling command of those dark, dangerous eyes. Slowly, struggling to hold her head erect, she walked towards him, until she was standing beside the bed. He slanted her a look of mocking satisfaction, reaching out his hand to stroke it up the length of her silk-clad thigh, drawing her forward to rest one knee on the bed beside him.

She had to swallow hard; he had loosened the collar of his pristine white shirt, and beneath it she could glimpse that smattering of rough male body hair at the base of his throat. A sudden urgent impulse to unfasten the rest of the buttons, to tear the fabric back from that wide, hard-muscled chest flooded through her, and he laughed softly, as if he could read her thoughts.

Still holding her captive with that dark, level gaze, he deftly unsnapped her suspenders, one by one. 'Take your stockings off,' he ordered, smiling in lazy anticipation. 'Slowly.'

She did as he ordered, slipping off her shoes and rolling the sheer silk stockings down over the slender length of her legs, inch by inch, as he watched her in lazy amusement, finally letting each one drop to the floor. Then he drew her forward again onto the bed, moving her to kneel across his lap.

She felt achingly vulnerable, knowing how nearly transparent the tight lace basque was, acutely conscious of the way it invitingly cupped her breasts and moulded intimately over every curve. Without thinking she lifted one hand to brush a strand of hair back over her shoulder, recognising the flame of interest in his eyes as the movement crushed one hardened nipple tautly against its lace constraint.

'Yes—a very attractive package,' he murmured. 'Now, how do I begin to unwrap it? Ah, yes—I see.'

There was a concealed zip that ran down the front, and he gave it a teasing little tug, letting the first few inches spill open. She drew in a ragged breath, and he smiled as he watched the tumultuous rise and fall of her breasts, freed from their tight confinement. Very slowly, savouring every centimetre of bare flesh that was revealed, he slid the zip all the way down, finally unhooking it and letting the frivolous garment fall loosely to the floor.

She felt a hot blush of pink steal up over her cheeks as he gazed at her, naked now apart from the choker of pearls at her throat and the tiny triangle of her white lace briefs. She had to fight the instinct to hang her head, cover her breasts with her hair, conceal the betrayingly pert rosebud peaks from his lingeringly intimate survey. But this was her part of the bargain—her body. And, contrary to what he thought of her, she didn't believe in reneging on a deal.

So instead she let her back arch slightly, conscious of the way it tipped those soft, naked curves invitingly towards him. Again that smile of lazy appreciation curved his hard mouth as he let his two hands stroke up over the peachy smoothness of her skin to reach for the firm, ripe swell, his palms rasping lightly over the taut nipples, sending shivering little shocks into her brain.

'So... No Louis,' he murmured, a note of husky satisfaction in his voice. 'No Mark Ransome. No one else's fingerprints at all.' He let his hand slide over her breast, marking out the place where he had left his own imprint, now faded away. 'Mine. And don't you ever forget it.'

Her eyes glittered back at him, icily resentful of his arrogant assumption of ownership. But then that was the way it was, she acknowledged wryly to herself. So far as he was concerned she had sold herself to him, for the right to go on living the extravagant lifestyle she was accustomed to. Well, let him go on thinking that—keeping her love a secret was her only weapon against his casual cruelty.

His long, clever fingers were moulding and caressing her naked breasts, toying with them, teasing the tender peaks with his thumb as he watched every shadow of response that flickered across her face. That, at least, she couldn't keep secret; she could never pretend indifference to his expert touch—her body would betray her every time. But that was okay—he had said that the basis of their marriage was sex. Let him think that the same thing went for her too. It was likely to be a hostile relationship, but at least it would never lack for fireworks!

'Such a very beautiful package,' he murmured, almost abstractedly. 'Breasts so neat and firm, with such pretty little nipples, all pink and dainty. Just the right size to fit in my hand—or in my mouth...'

He tipped her forward, and she caught her breath on a sharp little gasp as she felt his teeth graze devouringly around the ripe, aching swell of one breast, drawing it deep into his hot mouth, his rasping tongue swirling languorously around it, and then slowly he drew his lips back, holding the tender peak with a hungry suckling, savouring the sweetness of the succulent fruit.

Liquid heat was pooling in the pit of her stomach, and with an urgency born of a wanton need she began to scrabble at the buttons of his shirt, impatient in her frenzy to let her hands rove over the hard, hairroughened plains of his chest. He laughed, a husky growl, and suddenly he had caught both her wrists, tumbling her over to pin her beneath his weight, her hands captured above her head, a hot flame in his eyes.

But his shirt was loose and open, and she wanted him. She broke from his restraining hold, her arms sliding around him to draw him down to her, letting him crush her breasts against the unyielding wall of muscle and bone as her mouth opened invitingly beneath his kiss.

His mouth was hot and demanding, moving over hers, inciting her to respond, and their tongues sparred in fierce battle until at last he asserted his dominance, plundering deep into every sweet, secret corner of her mouth in a flagrantly erotic exploration, a foretaste of the possession to come. And she surrendered all that he asked, and more, her body supplicant beneath his, aching for him.

They had to break apart, both dragging raggedly for

breath, and he tangled his hands into her hair, his kisses tracing a scalding path along the line of her cheekbone, his sensuous tongue swirling into the delicate shell of her ear and finding the sensitive spot just behind the lobe, making her shiver with pleasure. And then on, down the vulnerable curve of her throat and over her collarbone, as she arched her body to offer him again the ripe, tender succulence of her breasts.

He slanted her a glance of wicked amusement, taunting her wantonness, but she didn't care. As his mouth closed over one rawly sensitised peak she closed her eyes, letting the exquisite sensations wash through her, melting her into a pool of liquid honey. He subjected each breast in turn to the same delicious torment, until she was sobbing with pleasure, lost in a world of shimmering darkness, everything beyond this moment obliterated from her mind.

And then she felt his hands move down, slipping beneath the taut white lace of her briefs. She couldn't even think of resistance, though a small tremor of apprehension ran through her as he drew them down over the curve of her hips, easing them from her ankles and tossing them away somewhere. Now she was completely naked beneath him, her thighs held slightly apart by his to allow him free access to the sweet crimson velvet between.

The first intimate touch of his fingers made her breath catch in her throat, and she opened her eyes wide, a little shocked by the thrill of watching his hand exploring there into the most secret, feminine core of her body. But that thrill was quickly overtaken by another, as with magical skill he found the tiny seed-pearl of pleasure, hidden deep within its moist velvet pleat, and stirred it into sizzling arousal, laughing softly at her helpless sobs of ecstasy.

And then... She felt him move, felt him stretch her thighs much wider apart, felt him shift his weight between them. She opened her eyes again to gaze up at him, suddenly—devastatingly—aware now of the full implications of her surrender. But there could be no going back—he had her exactly where he wanted her, both physically and metaphorically. She had no escape.

'So... This is the moment when I find out if you really were telling the truth,' he growled, that hard, sensual mouth smiling down at her in lazy mockery.

She felt a spark of anger. Did he *still* not believe her? She sensed the raw male power, only held in check by his iron will, and her eyes flashed defiance. 'Go on, then,' she taunted. 'Take me...'

She arched beneath him, grazing her fingernails down the length of his spine—and with a sudden shattering of that rigid control he thrust into her, deep and hard. For one fleeting instant it was like being stabbed by fire, and her body jolted in shock, a sharp cry breaking from her lips. But the pain shattered around her like sparkling diamonds, leaving her only with the precious knowledge that at last she really belonged to him.

'You crazy fool...!' He shook his head, kissing away the tear she hadn't known was trickling from the corner of her eye. 'I wouldn't have hurt you if you hadn't done that.'

'But then you would never have been really sure,' she whispered back. 'Now you know.'

'Yes.' He moved, slowly, carefully, thrusting into her again, deepening his possession. 'Now I know.'

Not all her most fevered dreams had prepared her for this. She moved beneath him, instinctively matching his rhythm as the heat built inside her, her spine arching to offer him the deepest penetration, thrilling to her body's submission to his hard male power. They were both breathing raggedly, their bodies slicked with sweat as the fever took them. He soon forgot to be gentle, but she didn't care—her head was spinning in a delicious vortex; an exquisite tension was coiling in the pit of her stomach...

And then with a sudden, shattering spasm the tension broke apart, and a torrent of molten gold flooded her veins, and with a last sobbing cry she felt herself falling, falling, wrapped up in Oliver's arms, until they both collapsed, exhausted, tangled up in the white satin sheets of the bed.

CHAPTER NINE

'Do YOU really want to go out tonight?'

Oliver stood in the doorway of Ginny's dressing room, leaning one wide shoulder lazily against the frame, watching her with dark, smoky eyes as she wriggled into the slim sheath of black that she had just unhooked from its hanger. Wearing only a white towel, slung low around his lean hips, his wide chest still sun-bronzed from their honeymoon and smattered from throat to navel with a sprinkling of rough male body hair, he was proving a serious distraction.

'Yes, I do,' she insisted, trying not to sound as if she was finding it hard to resist the temptation to change her mind. 'The ambassador is a charming man. Besides, we accepted the invitation—it wouldn't be polite to just not show up.'

'A charming man?' he repeated, coming up close behind her and slipping his hands around her body, letting them slide up with unmistakable intent towards her breasts. 'Do you mean attractive?'

'Of...course not,' she protested a little unsteadily. 'He's...old enough to be my father! I just...'

He laughed, lazily mocking. 'I love your beautiful breasts,' he growled huskily, bending his head to graze a path of kisses down the long curve of her throat. 'So firm and ripe... Do you know I can feel your nipples hardening right through your dress?' He plucked at the tender nubs, emphasising their raised contours through the softly draping fabric. 'Your body was made to be made love to—it responds so wantonly every time I touch you. Let's plead sickness—I can feel my temperature rising. I think I've got a fever coming on.'

She drew in a ragged breath, laughing a little unsteadily as she shook her head. 'No...Oliver, please...'

She had closed her eyes, briefly letting her head tip back against his shoulder as she gave herself up to the pleasure of his caress. It was such a sweet slavery she had sold herself into, but for the sake of her sanity she tried not always to surrender too easily. So with an effort of will she slipped out of his embrace, laughing a little unsteadily.

'Foster will be round with the car in a few minutes,' she reminded him. 'You'd better get dressed.'

He conceded a wry smile, watching her in the mirror as she brushed out her long dark hair. 'Put it up,' he insisted.

'Do you think so?' she queried, twisting it around her hand and holding it to the crown of her head. 'I wasn't going to bother.'

'Put it up,' he growled. 'You're only to wear it loose for me.'

In the mirror, she shot him a look of surprise. He was getting very possessive of her. Was that a good sign? 'Yes, oh lord and master,' she responded, boldly teasing. 'Your wish is my command.'

'That's right.' He caught her by the shoulders, drawing her back against him, his hard hands imprisoning her—a small show of strength to demonstrate that he was only half joking. 'And don't you forget it.'

For a brief moment their eyes clashed in the mirrored reflection, as he mockingly challenged her to refute his arrogant assertion. But, recognising the moment when her defiance turned to acquiescence, he let her go.

'Okay, I'll get ready,' he conceded. 'Black tie?'

'Of course.'

He went back to his own dressing room, leaving her to finish putting up her hair.

They had been married for just six weeks now—six weeks that had been as close to perfect as she had any right to hope for, having been fool enough to risk marrying him when she knew he wasn't in love with her. Their honeymoon—on a tiny Caribbean island, all white sand and palm trees and not a single other human inhabitant—had been pure, sybaritic bliss. So much so that they had extended it for a full week beyond the original two they had planned.

And it certainly seemed that he couldn't get enough of making love to her. A small smile curved her soft mouth as she recalled the magical nights wrapped up in his arms, the mornings of waking beside him in their wide bed, the many times when he had come in from work wanting her right then and there: once in the flower room, several times on the floor in the drawing room, and once—memorably, if a little uncomfortably—in the cloakroom off the hall where the raincoats and wellington boots were kept.

It didn't take her long to coil her hair up into one of the elegantly simple styles she often wore it in. Drawing down a few tendrils around her face to soften the effect, she concentrated for a few moments on putting on her make-up—just a lick of tinted moisturiser to enhance the light golden tan she had acquired, a soft smudge of grey-brown shadow around her eyes and a thickening coat of mascara on her long lashes, and slick of scarlet on her lips.

Jewellery? Not too much, she decided, evaluating her reflection in the glass. A simple rope of gold around her throat, plain hoops in her ears, and the golden bracelet Oliver had bought her on their return from their honeymoon—with a catch designed like a pair of handcuffs. And her rings, of course.

Slipping on her black evening sandals, she checked the reflection one last time. The dress was one of her favourite stand-bys for an evening like this—black silk jersey, cut with a flawless simplicity, it had shoestring straps and a neckline that dipped in a deep vee into the soft shadow between her breasts, the fabric skimming her slender figure all the way down to her ankles.

'Ready?'

Oliver had appeared again in the mirror behind her, and as she glanced at him she felt her heartbeat quicken. She hadn't yet quite got used to how good he looked in a dinner jacket—it was something about the way he wore it, with a casual panache that reminded her constantly that beneath its formal elegance was a hard-muscled male body not too far removed from its primitive origins. In seconds he could drop that urbane façade, and drag her ruthlessly off to his cave...

'What's amusing you?' he enquired, not missing the sensual smile that had curved her lips.

'Oh...nothing.' Resolutely she pushed the image aside, shrugging her slender shoulders in a gesture of casual dismissal as she reached to pick up her evening bag. But he must have caught the glitter of her erotic thoughts in her eyes.

'Nothing?' His laughter was lazy. 'You wouldn't have been thinking about what I was thinking about earlier, would you?'

'Of...course not.' But her tone was betrayingly husky. Quickly, before he could trap her in the room and wreck their plans for the evening, she swung her bag onto her shoulder by its long gold chain, and slipped past him. 'Come along—we'll be late,' she asserted, preceding him down the stairs.

By the time they reached the front door he was at her side. The elegant Rolls Royce was already waiting at the bottom of the steps, Foster standing beside it. He held the door open for her as she climbed into the back seat, sinking onto the luxurious Connolly hide upholstery with a small sigh of pleasure.

Oliver joined her, the glint of provocative humour in his eyes warning her that he wasn't going to let her off so easily. 'This is going to be one of those dreadful cocktail parties where everyone talks at once and the champagne's much too sweet,' he warned her dryly.

She felt a hot little quiver of anticipation run through her. 'We can…leave early if you like?' she suggested, a betraying tremor in her voice.

He laughed, low in his throat. 'I was thinking I might need some…entertainment while I'm there,' he responded. He reached a casual hand along the back of the seat, and before she had realised what he was going to do he had slipped one thin strap of her dress down over the curve of her shoulder, so that the fabric fell away loosely, revealing the ripe swell of her breast as it nestled in the taut cup of a lacy black basque. 'I wondered what you had on underneath that,' he murmured. 'I like it.'

'Don't!' she protested, darting an agitated glance towards Foster at the wheel as she quickly pulled the strap back up and tried to edge a little further away from him along the seat. Surely he wasn't planning to make love to her right here in the back of the car…was he?

He laughed in lazy mockery and leaned forward to snap down the blind that separated them from the chauffeur. And then, with a glint in his eyes that warned her not to resist him, he slipped the strap down again, and with one tantalising fingertip he traced the edge of the delicate lace across her honeyed skin, down into the soft shadowed valley between her breasts.

'What's wrong?' he taunted, an inflection of sardonic humour in his voice. 'Afraid I'll mess up your make-up before we get to the party?'

'I...'

Smiling that sorcerer's smile, he brushed his palm across her breast, so that she could feel it warm and firm through the sheer fabric of the basque. The tender peak was hardening, sensitised by the rasp of the constraining lace, its contour clearly visible as a taut bud of rose-pink, thrusting pertly against the delicate tracery of black.

For a brief moment she closed her eyes. She knew that it was useless to try to resist him—that would simply goad him into asserting his mastery over her. The only thing she could do was try to pretend that what he was doing had no effect on her—though her breathing was shallow and impeded as he rolled the tender nipple beneath his thumb, sending sizzling sparks through her brain.

The traffic was light, and the elegant car sped in well-suspended luxury through the suburban streets as the last of the evening shoppers wound their way home. Tipped back in the corner of the seat, through half-closed eyes Ginny could see people at bus stops, people waiting at crossings, and had to remind herself that through the smoked glass they couldn't see her—couldn't see that her husband had eased the black lace cup of the tight basque down to bare the full, ripe curve of her breast, pink-tipped, and was circling over it tantalisingly with the tip of one finger, until he succeeded in forcing from her a gasp of helpless pleasure, betraying her response.

'You know, your body is a never-ending source of delight,' he murmured, softly mocking. 'Particularly when you try to resist its desire to surrender to me. You can never quite manage it—and the moment when your control snaps is always such fun to watch.'

Her eyes were a narrowed glitter of resentment, but there was nothing she could do. He was plucking lightly at the tender bud, rolling it between his clever fingers, and her spine was melting. It probably wasn't wise to always give in to him so easily, but he knew too well how to demolish any defences she might try to build up, with just a touch, just a look. Her only relief was that he believed her pleasure to be as shallow as his—a purely physical thing, with no love attached.

And oh, it was such sweet pleasure. He had bent his head over her naked breast, his hot tongue lapping at the taut, tender peak, swirling around it and flicking at it with the tip, his hard teeth nipping at it teasingly, suckling at it with a deep, hungry rhythm, driving her to the brink of insanity. If he chose to make love to her now, she wouldn't know how to stop him.

Dimly she recognised the streets as they drew nearer to their destination. 'Oliver,' she pleaded in ragged desperation. 'Oliver...please... We're almost there.' But he only laughed, continuing the torment until the car had actually turned into Kensington Palace Gardens and drawn to a halt outside the tall wrought-iron gates of the embassy.

And then at last he lifted his head, his languorous smile mocking her as she struggled to straighten her disordered clothing. 'Such demure elegance,' he taunted. 'Concealing such a sinfully inviting body. Yes, we'll be leaving early—unless you want to risk having me drag you behind one of the potted palms and making love to you?'

Her green eyes flashed him a fulminating glare, but there was no time for any other response. Foster had opened the car door and she climbed gracefully out, brushing down her skirt. Her breast was still aching from his attentions, the tender nipple rawly sensitised, so that with every breath the rasping constraint of the tight basque was a delicious agony. How was she ever going to walk into the ambassador's sophisticated cocktail party with the memory of what he had done to her still so vividly imprinted on her flushed skin...?

As Oliver climbed out beside her she let her hand rest lightly in his arm, and together they walked up the short drive to the imposing front porch, politely greeting several acquaintances who were arriving at the same time.

He leaned his head down slightly towards her, as if making some casual, conversational remark. 'Do you know what I'm going to do to you when I get you home?' he rasped smokily. 'I'm going to strip you naked and throw you on the bed. And then I'm going to get some honey and I'm going to dribble it all over that delicious body—over your ripe, luscious breasts and your soft, slender, yielding thighs. And then I'm going to lick it all off, inch...by inch...by inch...' He laughed, low and husky, his warm breath fanning her shoulder and making her shiver. 'And then I'm going to make love to you so hard you won't be able to walk for a week.'

She drew in a sharp, deep breath, struggling to suppress the hot flame of scarlet that had risen to her cheeks. It took every ounce of will-power she possessed to be able to feign some kind of composure as a line of footmen—all of them ready to transform themselves into highly trained security guards at the slightest hint of alarm—bowed them politely into the imposing marble hall, and through into the sumptuous ballroom.

It was a glittering gathering—all the women in silk and diamonds, the men formal in dinner jackets, a few in military uniforms or traditional African or Arab robes. Waiters in trim white livery circulated with silver trays laden with glasses, expertly weaving their way through the jostling throng without ever spilling a drop.

Oliver had been right—everyone was talking at once, ignoring the five-piece band that was playing on a raised stage in one corner, and when he claimed them two glasses of champagne from a passing waiter she found that it was much too sweet. It was going to be a boring evening, but once they had circulated and talked to a few people maybe they would be able to slip away...

Her casual survey of the room was suddenly arrested by a familiar profile, over by the far door. Pale blonde hair, gleaming beneath the chandeliers, drawn smoothly back from cameo-like features, skin that was almost translucent: Alina. Aunt Margot had mentioned that she was expecting to leave the clinic this week, but Ginny had assumed that she would take things easy for a little while—perhaps go on holiday. She couldn't imagine that a noisy embassy party was an ideal form of convalescence.

She would have preferred their first encounter to have been in private—a family occasion, perhaps. Not here, in such a public place. But she had no time to worry about what might happen—the ambassador himself was bearing down on them, his exotic dark eyes sparkling.

'Ah, my darling girl!' he greeted her, sweeping her into a giant hug and bestowing a generous kiss on each cheek. 'How wonderful to see you! And Oliver, my good friend!' He seized Oliver's hand, pumping it warmly. 'And now you two people have married, I hear? Wonderful news, wonderful! You must cherish her, my friend,' he admonished solemnly. 'She is worth her weight in rubies! So many of these fine society ladies dabble in good works merely so that they may say to

their friends, "Look what I do." But my sweet Ginny…'
He lifted her hand to his lips in an extravagant gesture,
placing a kiss on her fingers. 'She gives her whole heart.'

Oliver smiled down at her, and to her surprise she
realised that there was no trace of the mockery she had
been expecting to see in his eyes. 'I know,' he responded
with a hint of pride.

The ambassador laughed indulgently. 'Ah, but you
would indeed,' he concurred. 'There is little which hap-
pens without Oliver Marsden knowing of it—is that not
so?'

'In general,' Oliver conceded, a slight note of constraint in his voice. 'But please excuse us—I have yet
to dance with my wife.'

'Of course, of course,' the ambassador boomed, waving them away. 'Enjoy yourselves, yes?'

Ginny glanced up searchingly at her husband as he
drew her onto the dance floor and into his arms, moving
her expertly to the music of the band. 'What did you
mean just now?' she asked.

He arched one dark eyebrow in bland enquiry. 'What
did I mean by what?'

She shook her head, refusing to be deflected by his
evasive tactics. 'You said, "I know",' she persisted.
'What do you know?'

'If you mean do I know about all the work you do for
charity, of course I do,' he responded, mildly amused.
'Did you think I didn't? I've been receiving regular bul-
letins on your activities for years.'

She blinked up at him, startled. 'You have?'

'Of course. Mostly from Margot, though some from
other sources as well.'

'Oh, really?' She shouldn't have been surprised, of
course, though she was a little annoyed that he hadn't

told her before. 'And what else did you receive reports on?'

'Oh...the state of your love-life,' he conceded, regarding her with teasing humour. 'Margot was ready to warn me if any of your affairs looked like turning into something more serious.'

'Oh?' Her eyes were sparking green fire. 'And what would you have done about it if they had?'

'Put a spoke in it, of course,' he responded with cool arrogance. 'I told you, I had no intention of letting you marry anyone except me.'

'Maybe you wouldn't have been able to stop me,' she countered, defiant—had he really sat calmly in New York, biding his time until he was ready, assured that there was no competition to concern him? 'I might have fallen in love with one of them.'

'Oh, I didn't think there was much danger of that. I knew you couldn't be too involved with any of them—in spite of all the lurid stories about your sexual adventures.'

'*What?*' She glared up at him. 'You knew they were lies? You *knew*?'

He laughed softly, drawing her closer into his arms. 'Let's just say I was aware that most of the sources of gossip were notoriously unreliable,' he conceded.

'You...' She struck him on the chest with her fist. 'You let me think you believed it all!' she protested, pretending annoyance to disguise the crazy surge of happiness in her heart.

'Well, I wasn't one hundred per cent sure,' he admitted, smiling wryly. 'Not until the first time I made love to you myself. You could have been faking a lot of things, but there was no way you could fake that look of innocent surprise at what was happening to you. I think that was the most beautiful moment of my life.'

She gazed up at him, feeling as though she was drowning in the depths of those liquid dark eyes. 'It was?' she whispered, dazed.

'Yes, it was.'

Ginny closed her eyes, letting herself rest her cheek against the hard wall of his chest, letting the music drift into her mind, mingling with the evocative musky scent of his skin to drug her mind. Maybe it was foolish of her to begin to hope, but she couldn't help it... Was it just the sexual possessiveness of a predatory male—or was it something more...?

An unwelcome voice cut into the velvet cloak of dreams. 'Why, Oliver—Ginny. How lovely to see you.'

Alina's smile was brittle, her eyes over-bright. And she had lost weight, making her almost too thin, her delicate features jagged, her skin taut and pallid, with a fine tracery of lines around her mouth. For the first time Ginny recognised the fragility that must have always lain hidden beneath that aura of self-assurance the older woman had always seemed to convey so effortlessly. If only she had known... maybe she would still have found it hard to forgive, but she might have understood.

She watched as Alina exchanged a kiss of welcome with Oliver, but though she felt a certain wary caution the jealousy that once would have sliced her like a knife was now gone. Oliver had never loved Alina. If he had, he would have married her. She was sure of that now— it had nothing to do with her own tentative hopes. And with it went the knowledge that Alina no longer had any power to harm her.

But there was still a degree of strain as the two of them exchanged air-kisses—and Alina's immaculately manicured hands felt like claws as they gripped Ginny's. She drew back, a shadow of that old patronising smile on her thin lips. 'Darling, what a lovely dress,' she mur-

mured. 'You're *so* brave to wear such a clinging fabric—
it can be so unforgiving.'

Which could be taken as a suggestion that it made her
look fat, Ginny mused dryly. But she ignored the remark.
Though it was true she had put on a little weight during
her honeymoon, she wasn't bothered—she never had to
think much about her waistline.

They exchanged a few minutes' polite conversation,
and then Alina glanced past them, smiling vaguely.
'Well, do excuse me,' she purred. 'There's someone
over there I *have* to talk to.'

She was gone, leaving Ginny to let out a secret sigh
of relief. It was perhaps a little odd that Alina had mentioned nothing of the wedding, but maybe it was just as
well. From beneath her lashes she slanted a searching
glance up at Oliver's face, but she could read nothing
of his thoughts. At least it seemed that he had been
proved right about it being best to get it all over and
settled while Alina was still in the clinic—she did seem
to have accepted the situation as it was.

But she had little chance to reflect further on the subject—they both had many friends and acquaintances at
the reception, and were soon accosted by a string of
people eager to discuss the latest news from Wall Street
or the newest boutique to have opened in Beauchamp
Place. It was beginning to look as if their plans for an
early departure were going to be thwarted.

Some time later in the evening they became separated—Ginny had been dancing, and when she glanced
back across the room she saw that Oliver had been hi-
jacked by a coterie of Taiwanese businessmen intent on
picking his brains. She flashed him a smile of fleeting
sympathy and eased herself around to a quiet corner beside one of the fluted pillars holding up the ceiling, collecting a glass of champagne on her way.

'Ah…Ginny.' A softly insidious voice spoke at her shoulder. 'I see you've finally tired of dancing for a while.'

She glanced round to find Alina beside her, smiling that cool little smile. 'Yes…' In spite of everything, it still took an effort of will to remind herself that she was no longer a gawky, naïve nineteen, and Alina the self-assured rival for Oliver's affections. 'It's a bit of a crush.'

'It is, isn't it?' The older woman flickered a glance at the two rings on the third finger of Ginny's left hand. 'It's a nice wedding ring,' she remarked on a note of casual interest. 'I prefer a simple band—those fancy carved ones can look so trumpery.'

Ginny conceded a faint smile that could have been taken for polite agreement—she didn't really want to get drawn into a conversation with Alina.

'I must admit,' the older woman continued, saccharine sweet, 'I was a little surprised at first to hear about the wedding. But then, when I reflected on it, I realised that perhaps it wasn't so surprising after all.'

'Oh…?' Ginny's response was wary; she sensed that Alina wasn't about to put a favourable slant on the situation.

'Well, after what he did to your father, I really thought the last thing you would do was marry him. But then you've always been in love with him, haven't you?'

Ginny frowned sharply. 'My father? What has Oliver got to do with my father?' she demanded.

'You didn't know?' Those blue eyes glittered like ice. 'Of course, I've known Oliver for a long time—I know just how ruthless he can be when someone crosses him. But I really didn't think he would take out his revenge on your father like that, making sure he lost all his money.'

'What are you talking about?' Ginny countered, reminding herself swiftly to be very suspicious of anything the older woman might tell her.

But Alina's smile was smooth. 'Do you know a man called Guy Prentiss?' she queried.

'Yes...' Ginny frowned again. 'He was the agent who put Daddy's name on the insurance syndicate that crashed.'

'He was a friend of Oliver's—they met in America. Oliver recommended him to several people, I believe— including your father. Later he warned the others off, in time for them to leave the syndicate as soon as the year was declared closed. But not your father. He was trapped on an open year, with massive potential losses—I gather it could be ten years or more before the underwriters will be able settle the outstanding liability.'

Ginny couldn't disguise her shock—not only at the older woman's accusations, but at her detailed knowledge.

Alina smiled kindly. 'I thought at first that he was just planning to hurt you by hurting your father. But I see now that he was playing a deeper game. You must have been in a terribly difficult position after your father died, with no money—it must have been really quite easy for Oliver to manipulate you into agreeing to marry him. And now he has you exactly where he wants you. I remember when he was younger he used to enjoy pulling the legs off spiders. He can be terribly cruel, you know.'

Ginny drew in a long breath, struggling to cling onto her reason. 'I...don't believe you,' she said. 'You lied to me before.'

Alina laughed sadly, shaking her head. 'I didn't lie— at the time I truly believed what I told you. But eventually I realised that he had never really loved me—I honestly believe he isn't capable of love. It isn't really his fault, I suppose. As a boy, he was so devoted to his mother, you see, and when she died...he was at such an impressionable age. Her dying would have seemed as if she was deserting him, and so he's never been able to relate to any other woman since. Oh, I know he's a wonderful lover.' A small smile of reminiscence curved her lips. 'But a man doesn't need to feel any emotion for a woman to enjoy having sex with her. But as for what he did to your father, of course you don't just have to believe me,' she added, deadly confident. 'Ask Peter.'

'Peter?' Alina's eyes widened. 'What does he know about it?'

'He knows about Oliver and Guy Prentiss. And if you want further proof you can ask Guy himself.' She slipped her hand into her bag and drew out a small white business card. 'That's his number. Give him a ring— have lunch with him. Ask him whatever you like. He has no reason to lie to you—his reputation has already been totally ruined.'

Ginny took the card, staring at it blankly as Alina slipped discreetly away. She didn't want to believe her, and yet...she had seemed to know so much about it. And Oliver *had* lied about how he knew about her father's crisis—he had said his father had told him, but Howard had insisted that they had never discussed financial matters. She had pushed that awkward anomaly to the back of her mind, but now...

Oh, she had little doubt that Alina was motivated by jealousy, but could she afford to ignore what could be a critical warning? Perhaps it would be wise to at least seek some independent corroboration from Peter—she could be sure that he at least wouldn't lie to her. And then there was Guy Prentiss, she reflected, glancing down with some distaste at the card in her hand. Her instinct was to throw it away, but instead she tucked it into her bag. She would speak to Peter first, though—he would probably be able to dismiss the whole thing as a pack of nonsense...

'Hello, beautiful. I saw your face across the crowded room, and I just had to come over. If you're not with anyone tonight, how about coming home with me? We could make beautiful music together.'

Ginny was forced to laugh at the appalling cliché, as a man's warm breath fanned the nape of her neck. 'I'm with my husband,' she responded demurely.

'And is he the jealous type?'

'Extremely.' She turned, smiling up into her husband's dark, teasing eyes. 'Or so he tells me.'

'And you'd better believe it,' he asserted, slipping a possessive arm around her waist. 'Come on, let's get out of here before anyone else tries to collar me about the price of aluminium.'

She was more than ready to agree—after what Alina had told her, she really didn't feel like putting on her usual smiling façade and making inane small-talk for the rest of the evening with a string of people curious about the unexpected revival of her relationship with Oliver after it had seemed so ignominiously dead and buried six years ago.

'I saw you chatting to Alina...?' Oliver remarked, a question in his voice.

'Oh, yes...' She shrugged her slender shoulders in a gesture of dismissal. 'Just...chitchat.' There was no need to tell him about her suspicions just yet—she would try to be more sure of her facts this time before she confronted him. She wouldn't repeat the mistakes of the past.

But as they rode home she was aware of a certain constraint that she hadn't felt since the intimacy of their marriage had lulled her into a state of blissful amnesia.

And that night, for the first time, she contrived to be in bed well before he was, feigning sleep. She felt him lean towards her, felt his hand brush lightly over the bare curve of her shoulder, but then he must have decided not to wake her, and, moving back to his own side of the wide double bed they shared, he read for a little while before turning the light out.

She lay very still and tense in the darkness, listening to the sound of his breathing. Had Alina told the truth this time? Had he really plotted against her father? And, if it was true, what sort of cruel revenge could he have planned for her?

CHAPTER TEN

THE restaurant was very discreet—the perfect place for a married woman whose husband was away on business to enjoy a secret assignation with her lover. Except that Ginny wasn't lunching with a lover. In fact the thing she would most have liked to do with the man sitting opposite her was to have him fitted with a pair of concrete boots and dropped into a murky part of the River Thames.

Unfortunately that kind of behaviour tended to be frowned upon by the police. And after all she *had* agreed to lunch—though her original plan had been a brief meeting in some anonymous car park or hotel lobby, fifteen or twenty minutes at the most. Then she could have driven quickly home and had a nice shower, and washed the smell of this encounter down the drain.

Guy Prentiss was extremely good-looking—tall and naturally broad-shouldered, with chiselled features and smartly coifed dark blond hair. Only a very critical eye could quibble at the rather obvious attentions of a blow-dryer, or suspect the assistance of a little mild bleach, and only the ill-willed could look forward to the day when those early signs of a double chin developed into full-blown jowls, and those crinkling blue eyes succumbed to bags and sags.

'It's been hell,' he was declaiming earnestly, between mouthfuls of langoustine in white wine sauce. 'I don't mind telling you. But what people don't seem to understand is that I've been as badly hit as anyone—if not worse! I've lost more than just money—I've lost my career, my reputation...'

But not his Armani suit or his Rolex Oyster watch, Ginny noted tartly.

'The sad thing is that a lot of those people who lost money were my friends—and now they're not even speaking to me. Some of them even cross the street to avoid me, and that hurts.' A whipped puppy could not have looked more hard done by. 'But I suppose I really can't blame them.' That was produced with a boyish smile—one he obviously expected to captivate her. 'The sad thing is, it needn't have happened. If they hadn't pulled the rug out from under us like that, we could have done a far better job of sorting out the mess than those goons they put in. I seriously doubt whether they even know how to read an underwriting account. Some of the figures they were coming up with were just plain bull...ah, just plain ludicrous.'

'How did you come to know my husband?' she enquired stiffly, weary of his self-seeking tirade.

'Ollie? Oh, I've known him for years—more years than I care to remember.' He laughed, inviting her to express astonishment that it could be so very long. 'I was doing a spell in the States with Tyler Warren—you know, the big securities house?' He dropped the name as if it was royalty. 'We managed to do each other a few favours—you know the sort of thing. I was able to introduce him to a few people, put a little investment his way, and he did the same for me.'

'And...my father?'

'Oh, yes.' He nodded, reaching into his memory. 'It was a couple of years after I'd come back from the States... Oh, excuse me.' It was the third time in twenty minutes that they had been interrupted by the mobile phone that lay on the table within convenient reach of

his hand. Ginny privately suspected that he paid someone to call him up, just so that he could look important,
half turning so that everyone in the restaurant could see
who it was snapping out terse instructions in some in-
comprehensible business school jargon.

How could her cautious, conservative father even
have let such an obvious wide-boy within a hundred
miles of his finances? she mused. Solely because Oliver,
whose business acumen he had always respected, had
introduced him, was the bitter conclusion.

'So, where were we?' He had put the phone down
again. 'Ah, yes—Ollie. As I was saying, it was pretty
much a lucky coincidence that we ran into each other
again. I'd been back from the States a couple of years
by then, and I was doing a little business with an investment trust in the City. One day they took me to meet
with their backers, and who should turn up but old Ollie!
Turns out he was on this side of the pond for a couple
of weeks...'

The mobile buzzed yet again—Ginny had to suppress
an urge to dunk it in her mineral water, along with the
slice of lemon.

'So Oliver introduced you to my father?' she persisted
when that call ended.

He nodded, taking another forkful of langoustine. 'I
told him I was looking to sign up more Names to the
agency, and he offered to set up a few meetings for me—
for the standard introductory fee, of course. The meeting
with your father... We did lunch, I believe, the three of
us—at the Davenport, if I recall correctly. Look, I made
damn sure all my investors understood the downside
risks,' he added defensively. 'But you don't make
money in this world unless you're willing to take a few
chances.'

'No doubt.' She felt as if her jaw would crack with

the tension knotting inside her, but she had all she needed to know. 'Well, thank you, Mr. Prentiss. You'll excuse me if I don't stay for coffee?' With a discreet glance she summoned the waiter, paying for the lunch with Oliver's credit card—there was a certain satisfying irony in that, she reflected as she signed her name with a vicious flourish.

He rose to his feet as she did, all smooth blond charm. 'What a pity you have to rush away,' he protested, that boyish smile winging out. 'I appreciate that you may have some reservations about me, but I'm sure if you let me take you out to dinner we can clarify any differences we may have. What do you say?'

She returned him a smile of pure honey. 'I'd rather have dinner with a colony of giant slugs,' she responded, and, swinging her bag onto her shoulder, she walked smartly out into the afternoon sunshine, drawing in a long deep breath of the clean fresh air.

Oliver had been away for a little over a week—a week that had frayed Ginny's nerves almost to the point of snapping. She had eaten little and slept less, her mind turning over and over everything that she had found out. Some obstinate part of her brain still didn't want to believe it, but the evidence seemed damning—Alina and Guy Prentiss she could have dismissed, but Peter's reluctant confirmation that Oliver *had* introduced several people to that…obnoxious man was not something she could ignore.

Oliver had called each evening, and it had been a further strain to speak to him as if nothing was wrong. She hadn't wanted to deal with this over the transatlantic telephone line—she wanted to see his face, see his eyes, when she accused him.

She wouldn't have been surprised to see that she had

worn a hole in the carpet, the way she had been pacing by the window in the dining room, watching for his car. A swift, agitated glance at her watch told her that it was almost nine o'clock. A carefully rehearsed script was playing over and over in her brain—this time she was going to get it *exactly* right.

It was raining slightly when she saw his headlights turn in through the front gates and approach slowly down the drive. She could feel her heart pounding—why was it taking him so long to turn off the engine and come into the house? It seemed like an age before the head-lights clicked off and the interior light came on, and she saw that tall, lithe figure straighten on the far side of the car, reaching back in to pick up his briefcase and then walking up to the house.

She was in the hall to meet him as he came in. He greeted her with a smile—which froze as he saw the glittering anger in her eyes.

'What's wrong?' he enquired sharply.

'Guy Prentiss.' She ground out the name through clenched jaws. 'You never told me you knew him.'

He sighed, setting his briefcase down on the hall table and tossing his car keys on top of it. 'If we're going to have a discussion about Guy Prentiss, do you mind if I sit down first and have a cup of coffee?' he queried tautly. 'I've just flown three thousand-odd miles, and I'm a little tired.'

'So you *did* know him?' The strain of the past week was threatening to tear her nerve-fibres to shreds. 'And you introduced people to him—for money? People who trusted you—you introduced them to that...*crook?*'

'I introduced a few people to him,' he conceded, his voice very even in contrast to her rising hysteria. 'Having looked very carefully into how his agency was being managed. At the time, I was perfectly satisfied that it was a sound proposition. It gave people whose money was tied up in a property or business the opportunity to generate a modest income. It was only later that I became concerned—he'd let himself get seduced by the prospect of making money faster, and taken on some very high-risk re-insurance liabilities.'

'So you advised people to pull out?' she demanded, her voice low and tense, her hands trembling.

'Yes, I did.' He was frowning. 'What's all this about? Who told you about Guy Prentiss anyway?'

'I've met him,' she informed him, her voice ice cold. 'He told me how you introduced him to my father. But you didn't advise my father to pull out when you warned the others. You deliberately let him be ruined. You…bastard!' She had promised herself that she would restrain her temper, but it came boiling up, exploding under the pressure of the past week. 'He spent the last years of his life in constant worry—and it was probably that which killed him…!'

He took a pace towards her, reaching out for her. 'Ginny, I…'

She shook him off violently, twisting away from him. 'Don't you touch me! Don't ever touch me again! I hate you! I'll hate you as long as I live!'

And, fleeing from the house, almost blinded by her tears, she stumbled down the steps and ran, ignoring his shout. 'Ginny…! Come back…!'

She had no idea where she was going—she just ran, gasping for breath, her footsteps crunching the gravel of the drive. He was close behind her, catching at her arm, but she swung free. She had almost made it to the gate, but he had dodged past her, blocking her way. Desperate, she swerved, finding a gap and darting though it, out into the road…

The headlights were bright, dazzling, filling her whole

field of vision. She heard the squeal of brakes, heard Oliver's horrified cry. 'Ginny...!'

'Ginny...?'

She sighed, wishing he would just leave her alone—she had the mother and father of all headaches. And small wonder with all those lights—flashing lights, red and blue—and all that noise and fuss. But it had been quieter for a while now; the light was a steady, diffused white and the noises were soft—a rhythmic pinging to the left of her somewhere, an occasional metallic echo, sometimes even voices. And scents...a medicated sort of smell, sharp like pine-needles—and roses. Yes, definitely roses. She turned her head, trying to see the roses.

'Ginny?' It was Oliver's voice again, taut, anxious. 'Ginny, please come back.' Low, compelling... 'Please, Ginny. I love you.'

Huh—as if she'd be stupid enough to fall for that one. She had been once—years ago. But not any more, buster. No way. Not with what she knew about him now.

'Ginny, sweetheart, please... Just open your eyes.'

'Don't touch me!' She wanted to shout it, but somehow it just came out as a croak.

She blinked in confusion, disorientated by the light. Oliver was close to her, smiling, those deep, dark eyes warm as buttered toast—he didn't seem to have heard what she had said. And for some reason she felt suddenly weak, aching all over, dizzy—and she needed him to care for her, more than anything else in the world. She tried to reach out her hand to him, but it felt so heavy... But he took it anyway, clasping it in his strong one, and she managed some kind of wobbly smile.

'Oliver...?' She didn't seem to be able to raise her voice above a whisper.

'Yes, sweetheart. Welcome back.' He was squeezing

her hand, and she was puzzled to see the sparkle of something that looked like a tear at the corner of his eye. 'Try to sleep now.'

She wanted to tell him that she had been asleep for the past couple of hours, but it seemed like too much effort to speak, so she just let her eyes drift shut again, still clinging to his hand, a small glow of happiness inside her. Oliver was here, and everything would be all right.

When she woke again, the scent of roses was still there. She breathed it in, warily exploring the inside of her head, but the sharp pain that had been there before seemed to have subsided into a dull ache. The rest of her felt a little better too, and she sighed with relief, easing herself into a more comfortable position before she risked opening her eyes.

'Good morning.' Oliver was sitting beside the bed, holding her hand in his, smiling at her.

She smiled back a little uncertainly. She had a vague recollection of something badly wrong, but she didn't want to bother thinking about that for the moment. 'You look terrible,' she murmured. In fact he looked as if he hadn't slept for a month, and he was badly in need of a shave. 'Have you been here all night?'

He laughed, that low, husky laugh she had always liked so much. 'I've been here all day and all night for the past week,' he responded wryly. 'You've been in a coma.'

She frowned at him, puzzled. 'I have?' She closed her eyes again—and saw, in dazzling brilliance, those headlights heading straight for her, and behind them the dark silhouette of a car roof. 'There was a car...'

'He couldn't do a thing.' He squeezed her hand between both of his. 'I never want to live through a moment like that again as long as I live.'

She smiled, reaching out a little unsteadily to brush back a wayward strand of his normally well groomed hair that was falling across his forehead. 'My head aches.'

'I'm not surprised,' he conceded. 'You had a blood clot on your brain—they had to operate.' He touched her head with a gentle hand, stroking it, and she frowned at the odd way it felt. 'They had to cut your hair off,' he told her quietly.

Her eyes widened in horror, and she reached up—to feel a kind of soft down where her long hair should be. 'My hair...!' She drew in a sharp breath, reminding herself quickly that it could have been so much worse. 'I must look awful,' she murmured.

He shook his head, lifting her hand to his lips and laying a kiss on the inside of her wrist. 'You look absolutely beautiful to me,' he asserted—and she knew by the low note of sincerity in his voice that he meant it.

With a small sigh of happiness she closed her eyes again, and drifted into sleep.

When she woke for the third time Oliver was still there, in a chair beside the bed, his head resting against the high back and his eyes closed, his mouth slightly open as he breathed slowly, asleep. He looked exhausted, and her heart creased with concern. Had he really sat here for all those nights, beside her bed, worrying about her?

She turned her eyes to glance briefly around the room she was in. It was a small private room, decorated in restful shades of pink and lilac. Beside her there was a heart monitor on a trolley, turned off now—it must have been that she could hear pinging before she had properly woken up. And there were flowers—tubs of them—on the windowsill, on a low cupboard against the far wall, on the table beside her bed. There was a vase of deep red roses, their petals like velvet, their fragrance sweet on the air. There were a dozen of them—she counted.

Her gaze slid back to Oliver again, and she watched him for a moment, fascinated by the soft shadow of his long lashes against his hard cheekbones, the curl of his hair around his ears. She had never really been able to study him like this before, to see the way sleep smoothed away the lines of arrogance, of that iron self-control, leaving him looking...almost vulnerable.

He had said he loved her—she hadn't dreamed that. And some instinct deep inside her told her that he was telling the truth. He had even said she looked beautiful with all her hair cut off—heavens, the poor man must be besotted! She put up her hand again to touch the fine down, feeling for the dressing above her right ear.

She must have taken quite a knock, she reflected ruefully. Fortunately her mind seemed to have blanked out the actual moment of impact—except for that single, almost photographic image of the dazzling headlights and the car roof, etched onto the back of her eyes.

The minute she stirred Oliver woke, his eyes anxious, and then smiled as he saw her awake. She smiled back at him, almost shyly. He loved her—after all these years, it wasn't very easy to take that in. 'Hi,' she greeted him, finding a little more strength in her voice now.

'Hello.' He leaned forward and took her hand. 'How are you feeling?'

'Oh...' She took a quick inventory of her aches and pains, and summarised with, 'So-so. Better, I think.'

'Good. Would you like some orange juice?'

'Thank you.'

He poured a glass and held it for her—although she tried, she didn't seem to have the strength to hold it herself. 'Not too much,' he cautioned. 'You haven't eaten for a week.'

And not much for the week before that either, she reflected, shreds of memory tugging at the fringes of her mind. The last time she had sat down for a meal—though she hadn't eaten much of it—was...when she had had lunch with Guy Prentiss...

'Guy Prentiss...' All the memories came flooding back, swirling into her aching head. So many contradictions—too many for her to work out.

'Ginny, I didn't introduce your father to Guy Prentiss,' Oliver told her, his words softly insistent. 'He lied to you. I had no idea your father was one of the Names on his agency—not until the inquiry. It wasn't even Guy Prentiss who signed him up—it was his partner, Charles Fleming, many years ago, before Guy even became involved. The evidence is all in the transcript of the hearings.'

'But...why did he tell me that?' she questioned. 'He had nothing to gain—he's already lost everything. And *you* lied to me,' she added. 'You told me you found out about my father from Howard, but Howard told me they never discussed financial matters.'

'I know. At the time, I didn't think you'd believe my explanation. You see, it was me who blew the whistle on Prentiss, and brought the whole house of cards he'd built tumbling down. And in the process, unavoidably, caused a lot of innocent people to lose a great deal of money. I couldn't warn them all, but I felt a responsibility for those I'd advised. If I'd known your father was in it...'

He sighed, a shadow passing across his eyes. 'It's a very difficult decision to call. The run-off game is like playing pass-the-parcel with a ticking bomb. If the year of the account is closed, then anyone who pulls out of the syndicate at that point is safe—all their liabilities are at an end. But if the long-term risks were underestimated, they are passed on to whoever is signed up to the next year.'

'And the bomb could blow up in their faces?'

He nodded. 'If at the end of the next year the under-writers can't decide on a re-insurance figure, the year is left open—and the liabilities can run and run. That was what happened, and it led to the inquiry. Prentiss was damned lucky to get away without facing a criminal prosecution, but he's never forgiven me. That was why he lied to you—he saw in you an opportunity to get his revenge.'

'Revenge... Alina said that was why you married me. For revenge.'

'Alina?' A wary note had crept into his voice. 'What has Alina got to do with it?'

She slanted him a swift glance, regretting that she had mentioned his stepsister's name. 'Oh...nothing,' she de-murred evasively.

'Ginny, what did Alina have to do with it?'

She shook her head, too weak to resist the quiet com-pulsion of his voice. 'She... It was she who told me you'd introduced Guy Prentiss to my father—she gave me his business card. I wouldn't have believed either of them, only...I asked Peter, and he said you *had* intro-duced a few people to him.'

He groaned as if in pain. 'The sly little... I should have known she would try to cause trouble—I should have warned you. It was her jealousy that sowed the seeds of all the damage the first time.'

She glanced up at him in surprise. 'You...knew about that?'

He nodded. 'From the minute she knew you were coming to New York she set out to meddle. I thought I'd made it clear to her that first night, when she showed up at my apartment while I was collecting you from the airport, that she wasn't to do anything to hurt you. I thought she'd got the message—but then I got that phone call, the night I was supposed to be taking you to the Richmond.'

'I remember,' Ginny murmured, brushing her hand over his.

'She told me that she was going to take an overdose,' he went on grimly. 'I spent all damned night trying to find her—she ran me ragged all over the city in some kind of bizarre paper-chase, until finally I caught up with her in some bar in Queens. Drunk, or stoned—I don't know which. I managed to persuade her to check into a clinic—and then I came home. To you. After the hell I'd been through, you were like a gift from heaven—all...sparkle and life.'

She couldn't help but laugh at that description of her. 'You make me sound like a Roman candle!' she teased.

He chuckled, shaking his head. 'I was head over heels in love with you. I knew I shouldn't rush into asking you to marry me that night. You were so young... But I'd been patient a long time, and I just wanted you so much.'

'You...did?'

He laughed in wry self-mockery. 'Remember the time I came to pick you up from school? You were about seventeen at the time, all legs and attitude, swinging your hair around and driving me half-crazy. I'd never thought of myself as a cradle-snatcher, but it was all I could do to control myself that afternoon. Margot guessed it, of course—she's one very shrewd lady.'

'Margot knew? But...didn't she want you to marry Alina?'

He shook his head decisively. 'No—not at all. She knew it would be disastrous. Alina's never been... exactly stable, even as a teenager. The damage stems from her father. He was diagnosed as manic-depressive, and although she hasn't actually got the same condition it was the effects of his illness that created her problems. One minute she was his little princess, the next he wouldn't even speak to her. And then he committed sui-cide—she was only ten years old.'

'I...didn't know. At least, I gathered from Aunt Margot that she'd been in a clinic before, but I didn't know any of that.'

'Your father never told you?'

'No. But then I was just a child when Aunt Margot married Uncle Howard. And later... Well, it would have been all old history by then. And he never was one to go in for gossip.' She slanted him a slightly crooked smile. 'Actually, Alina told me that it was you who was psychologically disturbed by losing your mother. She told me you saw it as a desertion, and had never been able to relate to any other woman since.'

He laughed rather harshly. 'Typical Alina psycho-babble,' he dismissed. 'Of course I was very upset, but my father handled it very well. And so did Margot. She never tried to take my mother's place—she's always been more of a friend. In fact it was her I talked to after that disastrous engagement ended. She advised me that it was probably because you were a little too young—and perhaps that your father and mine had put rather too much pressure on you with their clever little conspiracy.'

'Oh, no—it wasn't that!' She glanced up at him a little uncertainly. She didn't really want to tell him the truth—it made her look stupid, and Alina vicious. But while they were clearing the air she might as well get it over with. 'It was Alina,' she confessed. 'She told me that you were really in love with her, and that you would have married her if she could have had children—but she couldn't, so you were marrying me instead. To provide you with an heir.'

He stared at her in blank astonishment. 'What a load of…nonsense!' he declared. 'And you believed her?'

'Well… Not entirely, not right away. But… You *had* spent a lot of time with her, and…then when I came down and found you on the terrace with her, with your arms around her, telling her that our getting married wouldn't make any difference…'

Enlightenment dawned in his eyes. 'So *that's* why she insisted I go out onto the terrace with her and started getting all weepy, saying I wouldn't be her brother any more! I'm afraid she was very good at playing on my guilt—I *had* been quite attracted to her at first, but it had been no more than teenage puppy-love, and I grew out of it pretty damn quick when I realised how clingy and demanding she could be. But when I told her it was over, she took an overdose—the first of many—and I felt as though it was all my fault.'

Ginny squeezed his hand in concern. 'Oh, no—it couldn't have been. You were only young yourself.'

'I know—that's what Margot told me. And later, when Alina went off and got married, I thought it would all be all right, that she had got over it. But she never really let go. Oh, most of the time she played it as the sister, getting me running around after her every time she had a crisis. I just hope that now she's gone back to her husband things will settle down.'

'She's gone back to her husband?' Ginny repeated, startled.

He nodded. 'Her first husband. He's always been very concerned for her—he was more of a father figure, which is probably just what she needed. It's been on the cards for some time—he came over to England and visited her a great deal while she was in the clinic this last time. And now I think that perhaps your accident, and her realising that she was partly responsible for it, has brought her to her senses a little. They flew back to Texas on Thursday.'

Ginny breathed a sigh of relief. 'Good. I hope she'll be happy—if only because that will mean she won't cause any more trouble.'

Oliver nodded, stroking her hand. 'So... That just leaves...you and me,' he remarked wryly. 'We haven't made a very good job of it so far, have we?'

'No...' She lowered her lashes, suddenly a little shy. 'I...could never believe you could be in love with me,' she murmured. 'You...never actually said it, you know. Not even the first time, when you asked me to marry you.'

He had turned her hand over, and was tracing the lines of her palm with the tip of one finger. 'Didn't I? No, I know I didn't. I don't really know why...I suppose because I'd been turned off the words by Alina—she used them like some kind of meaningless mantra. But I should have realised that you needed to hear them. That night— you know, when you threw the ring back at me and ran off the terrace? I was sorry I'd spoken to you so sharply, but Alina had just about run me ragged—I had no patience left for anyone. I was going to come after you and apologise, and tell you then that I loved you, but I thought I ought to give you a few moments to calm down first. Besides, I was trying to find the stupid ring, so I could give it back to you,' he added with a wry laugh. 'It had rolled under some leaves, and it took me ages to find it. I'd just picked it up and was coming to look for you when there was all that uproar—and it was too late.'

A single wet tear was starting to trickle down her cheek, in sorrow for all the unhappiness and wasted years. 'I wish you'd come anyway. But maybe...I *was* too young for you then. I don't know. But you broke my heart.'

'Oh, my love...' He stroked his hand over the soft down on her head. 'I wouldn't have hurt you for the world.'

Her soft mouth quirked into a smile. 'You made a pretty good job of it when you came back to London,' she accused. 'I thought you hated me!'

'Sometimes I almost thought I did,' he admitted, laughing wryly. 'You'd grown from a charming girl to a beautiful woman—all that sparkle had turned to fire. I didn't know how to handle you—and I was afraid that after everything had gone so badly wrong before I couldn't make you love me again. But the first time I kissed you I realised there was one avenue that was *definitely* still open to me.'

Her eyes sparkled as she slanted him a wicked glance. 'Well, you certainly...'

There was a light tap on the door, and it opened without ceremony to admit the consultant, in a slightly rumpled grey suit, a stethoscope dangling loosely from his top pocket. 'Ah, Mrs Marsden...! So, how are we feeling this afternoon. A little better, I trust?'

She smiled wanly, and managed a careful nod. 'Apart from a headache.'

'Ah, that will pass. Let me see...' He took an instrument from his pocket and leaned over her, shining a pinpoint of light into first her right eye, then the left. 'Well, that seems to be okay. You've been quite lucky, you know. No actual damage, and no other bones broken. And there's no reason to suppose the baby will have come to any harm, not at this early stage. We picked up the heartbeat on the scan yesterday—quite strong.'

'The...baby?' she repeated blankly.

'Oh, yes. Didn't you know? About eight weeks from conception, I'd say.' He pulled a piece of card from his pocket. 'Here's the sonogram. Not much to see at this stage, I'm afraid. Just that little black dot, there.' He pointed with his finger. 'Well, if everything's okay, I'll be off—I'll pop in and see you again in the morning. Goodbye.'

And he was gone, closing the door behind him, leaving Ginny staring at the fuzzy pattern of black and white smudges on the sonogram he had handed her, trying to be sure exactly which black dot he had indicated was the baby.

Oliver chuckled with laughter. 'It's hard to tell, isn't it?' he remarked. 'It's there.'

She gazed up at him, still stunned. '*You* knew?'

He nodded, smiling in unmitigated delight. 'They asked me if you could be pregnant, and of course I told them that I hoped so. So they did a scan—they did one on the second day, but it wasn't conclusive, so they repeated it yesterday. It was amazing—this little tiny black dot, and it was thumping away nineteen to the dozen! Apparently the heart beats very quickly to start with, and then it gradually slows down to normal. You really didn't know?'

She bit her lip, lowering her lashes. 'I...was beginning to suspect. But...'

He frowned sharply. 'Aren't you pleased?' he queried anxiously.

'Yes...' But her voice sounded a little uncertain. 'Yes, of course I am. It's just...Alina said that was the reason you wanted to marry me—to have an heir.'

He took her hand firmly in his, taking the sonogram from her and laying it down on the bedside cabinet. 'Ginny, listen to me. You can't trust anything Alina has ever said—don't you realise that by now? And as for the baby—of course I want a baby with you. Not just an heir, but a family—children. But that wasn't why I married you. I married you because I love you. Truly, honestly, wildly, irrevocably—for the rest of my life, I love you. Does that convince you?'

She lifted her eyes to gaze up into his, a tremulous smile beginning to curve her soft mouth. 'As much as that?' she whispered, feeling a small glow of joy rooting itself deep in her heart. 'Even with no hair?'

'Even with no hair!' he confirmed, lifting her hand to his lips and dropping a tender kiss on the inside of her wrist. 'You're the most beautiful woman in the world, Mrs Marsden, and I love you.'

She sighed, closing her eyes, content to slip back into sleep again. 'You're crazy,' she breathed happily. 'But I love you too.'

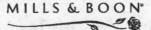

This month's irresistible novels from

Temptation®

SEDUCING SAVANNAH Gina Wilkins

Southern Scandals

Savannah McBride scandalized her small town thirteen years ago
when she found herself unwed and pregnant. Now she's had a
passionate holiday affair which she thinks is over. Until her
handsome lover turns up on her doorstep...

NIGHT RHYTHMS Elda Minger

Blaze

Meg Prescott's visit home was supposed to be a simple school
reunion. Until lean and sexy Daniel Willett strolled into the bar.
At sixteen she'd carried a torch for this rugged loner—and the
flame is still burning...

DOUBLE TAKE Janice Kaiser

When Arianna Hamilton's ex helps her out in a dangerous
situation, he shows a side of himself she's never seen before.
Suddenly he seems tough, sexy, alluring... What had happened to
the nice banker she'd left at the altar because he was *boring*...?

HEAD OVER SPURS Heather Warren

Callie Masters is not pleased to be spending her entire summer
designing houses in the middle of nowhere. But the rugged
McCall brothers are rather more interesting than she anticipated.
In fact, Rock McCall is the sexiest man she's ever met...and the
most accident-prone!

EMILIE RICHARDS

THE WAY BACK HOME

As a teenager, Anna Fitzgerald fled an impossible
situation, only to discover that life on the streets was
worse. But she had survived. Now, as a woman,
she lived with the constant threat that the secrets of
her past would eventually destroy her new life.

1-55166-399-6
AVAILABLE IN PAPERBACK
FROM SEPTEMBER, 1998

JASMINE CRESSWELL

THE DAUGHTER

Maggie Slade's been on the run for seven years now.
Seven years of living without a life or a future because
she's a woman with a past. And then she meets Sean
McLeod. Maggie has two choices. She can either run,
or learn to trust again and prove her innocence.

"Romantic suspense at its finest."

—Affaire de Coeur

MIRA®

1-55166-425-9
**AVAILABLE IN PAPERBACK
FROM SEPTEMBER, 1998**

CHRISTIANE HEGGAN

SUSPICION

Kate Logan's gut instincts told her that neither of her clients was guilty of murder, and homicide detective Mitch Calhoon wanted to help her prove it. What neither suspected was how dangerous the truth would be.

"Christiane Heggan delivers a tale that will leave you breathless."

—Literary Times

1-55166-305-8
AVAILABLE IN PAPERBACK
FROM SEPTEMBER, 1998

4 FREE
books and a surprise gift!

We would like to take this opportunity to thank you for reading this Mills & Boon® book by offering you the chance to take FOUR more specially selected titles from the Presents™ series absolutely FREE! We're also making this offer to introduce you to the benefits of the Reader Service™—

> ★ FREE home delivery
> ★ FREE gifts and competitions
> ★ FREE monthly newsletter
> ★ Books available before they're in the shops
> ★ Exclusive Reader Service discounts

Accepting these FREE books and gift places you under no obligation to buy, you may cancel at any time, even after receiving your free shipment. Simply complete your details below and return the entire page to the address below. *You don't even need a stamp!*

YES! Please send me 4 free Presents books and a surprise gift. I understand that unless you hear from me, I will receive 6 superb new titles every month for just £2.30 each, postage and packing free. I am under no obligation to purchase any books and may cancel my subscription at any time. The free books and gift will be mine to keep in any case.

P8YE

Ms/Mrs/Miss/Mr .... Initials ....
BLOCK CAPITALS PLEASE

Surname ....

Address ....

....

.... Postcode ....

Send this whole page to:
THE READER SERVICE, FREEPOST, CROYDON, CR9 3WZ
(Eire readers please send coupon to: P.O. BOX 4546, DUBLIN 24.)

Offer not valid to current Reader Service subscribers to this series. We reserve the right to refuse an application and applicants must be aged 18 years or over. Only one application per household. Terms and prices subject to change without notice. Offer expires 31st March 1999. As a result of this application, you may receive further offers from Harlequin Mills & Boon and other carefully selected companies. If you would prefer not to share in this opportunity please write to The Data Manager, P.O. Box 236, Croydon, Surrey CR9 3RU.

Mills & Boon Presents is being used as a trademark.

MILLS & BOON®

Emma Darcy

The Collection

✻ ✻ ✻ ✻

This autumn Mills & Boon® brings you a powerful
collection of three full-length novels by an
outstanding romance author:

Always Love
To Tame a Wild Heart
The Seduction of Keira

Over 500 pages of love, seduction and intrigue.

Available from September 1998